Balance of Body
Balance of Mind

A Rolfer's Vision of
Buddhist Practice in the West

by

Will Johnson

Humanics Trade Paperbacks
Atlanta, Georgia

Humanics Trade Paperbacks is an imprint of Humanics Limited

Humanics Trade Paperbacks
P.O. Box 7400
Atlanta, GA 30357
Humanics Trade Paperbacks is an imprint of Humanics Limited

PRINTED IN THE UNITED STATES OF AMERICA

Library of Congress Cataloging in Publication Data

Johnson, Will
Balance of Body, Balance of Mind/Johnson, Will
p. cm.
Includes bibliographical references.
ISBN 0-89334-163-0
1. Mind and body therapies. 2. Equilibrium (Physiology) — Health aspects.
3. Mental Health — Religious aspects — Buddhism. 4. Health — Religious
aspects — Buddhism. I. Title
RC489.M53J65   1992
613 — dc20   92-34218
                                                       CIP

Table of Contents

Dedication

*This book is dedicated to my mother and father
in recognition of their love, patience, and support.*

Where do the ideas in a book like this originate? While it is easy for me to cite my major sources of influence, it is not so easy to determine where that influence ends and my contribution begins. I have been fortunate to have had a number of outstanding teachers from within both the somatic and Buddhist fields; they represent, at the very least, the matrix out of which the vision of this book has grown. For any inaccuracies that may have arisen in the way in which I have interpreted, combined, and shaped these teachings, I alone accept responsibility.

My most influential teachers of the body have been Ida Rolf, Emmett Hutchins, and Judith Aston. The highly individualistic, sometimes cantankerous, and always dynamic memberships of the Rolf Institute and the Guild for Structural Integration have been a constant source of nourishment, amusement, and stimulation. I would also like to acknowledge all of the many clients with whom I have had the privilege of working over the years. Each, in his or her own way, has shown me so much. In addition, there have been somatic therapists from many other traditions; we are all working with a piece of the puzzle and continue to influence and enrich one another.

The other major source from which this book draws in depth is the tradition of Buddhism and, in particular, the psychological model that tradition has so courageously and elegantly developed. My teachers of meditation, so different in their manner and approaches, have included Ruth Denison, S. N. Goenka, Koon Kum Heng, Jack Kornfield, Bhagwan Shree Rajneesh, and Tarthang Tulku.

Les Conner, Bill Hoth, Peter Melchior, and Thomas Hanna have contributed so much in the way of enthusiasm and editing, the two "e" words that are so helpful to a writer in his attempts to see a project through to its best possible conclusion. The editors at Humanics Publishing Group have been significant allies in the fine tuning of the manuscript. Finally, I wish to make mention of five very special people in my life: Lyn, who shares with me the vision of this book; Phil, with whom it originated; Kavita, through whom it was shown to be accurate; and Kailas and Jamie, who test it every second step along the way.

Introduction

At many times during the writing of this book I have felt like the point of confluence where two separate river systems join together to become one. The sources from which these systems originate could scarcely be further removed from each other; their points of origin are separated not only by great distance, but by time as well. However, the currents that determine their directional flow have brought them ever closer together, and they are now positioned to merge their contents into a single, common stream. I respect both of these systems; each in itself is worthy of prolonged study and concentration. Where this study has led me, however, is to discontinue viewing them separately, in isolation from one another, but instead to focus on the denominators common to both and on how they can ultimately be seen to converge. While each system has itself been extensively documented and defined, the way in which they have been combined here and the vision in which that combination has found expression are, to the best of my understanding, new. I do not view my role as creating something where there was nothing before, but simply as acknowledging a convergence of systems, the discovery of whose linkage appears to me to have been inevitable. An explorer does not create anything, but simply comes upon what has always been there. Until we learn of the discovery, however, the possibility of its existence may never occur to us.

The first of these systems is the psychological model that was originally forged by Siddhartha Gautama (563-483 B.C.), later known simply as the Buddha, and subsequently refined over twenty-five centuries through the experimentation of countless practitioners. The second is the recently developed tradition of Western therapy that has come to view the structure and experience of the physical body as a key to the creation of true mental health and well-being. Through their encounter it becomes clear that each possesses the ability to inform the other, that each can contribute clarification to the other's path of inquiry, and that each, in fact, holds something of a missing piece vital for the completion of the other. As one flows into the other, both are transformed.

Just as individual bodies differ as to their degree of flexibility, so too do different philosophical systems and approaches to the art of living. The teachings of the Buddha, collectively known as the Buddhist *dharma*, constitute a wonderfully flexible body of knowledge. This flexibility has allowed the *dharma*, as it spread over distance and time from the place and moment of its inception, to incorporate into its body of practice the prevailing psychological attitudes of the cultures into which it moved without sacrificing any of its essential nature. Moving northward across the Himalayas, the *dharma* encountered the animistic vision of Bon, and the result was the rich and vivid cosmology of Tibetan Buddhism. Moving eastward into China, and ultimately on to Japan, it was transformed through its contact with Taoism, and the result as we know it today is Zen.

The migrations of the *dharma* are not unlike a river overflowing its banks in search of yet another body of water with which to merge and into which to empty itself. Once again this migration is occurring, this time to the fertile soil of the West. It is not possible to determine with any certainty what the outcome of this encounter will be. Several generations of experimentation and sifting will be required before a truly indigenous form of practice will emerge. It is not at all difficult, however, to make some general observations about the prevailing winds and psychological climate that so profoundly affect the condition of the soil—our very minds and bodies—into which the *dharma* is implanting itself.

It is clearly a time of transition. The old crop has borne its fruit and is turning itself back into the ground; the new growth has not as yet appeared to establish itself. The ethics of the Judaic-Christian vision remain intact, but the traditional comforters and mediators of this vision, the rabbi and the priest, have had to relinquish some of their authority to a new intermediary, the psychotherapist. The functions that these mediators perform may appear to be similar in many respects, but their interests, as well as their methods of investigation, are changing in fundamental and significant ways.

Much of the focus of the old psychology is our relationship with matters and forces beyond ourselves. To this end, it demands much in the way of faith and belief and offers very little in the way of direct revelatory experience. The new psychology, on the other hand, emerging as it has out of a scientific mold, tends to shy away from anything that it cannot verify. It has dedicated itself to the clarification of experience here and now, but in its infancy the nature of that experience is still largely unformed. Like a child who has recently learned to walk, however, it has ventured far enough along to realize that the full spectrum of human experience is not just limited to those modes of behavior that can be verified in a laboratory. The whole domain of the numinous, that level of experience whose certainty relies on intuitive knowing rather than logical analysis, is gradually being recognized as a valid extension of the new psychology's interests. We are coming to realize that, in matters of the psyche, there is much more that needs to be explored and ultimately integrated than initially meets the eye. But where should we look? And what exactly are we looking for? These are the questions that so directly confront the contemporary Westerner who contemplates these important matters.

It is at this very formative moment that the Buddhist *dharma*, which has pondered these questions for twenty-five hundred years, is presenting itself on Western shores. The wealth of psychological insight that the *dharma* brings with it is almost over-whelming as it deftly bridges the gap between the immediately verifiable and the numinous. Not just content with providing theoretical clues, the *dharma* offers a host of exercises and techniques designed to enable the practitioner to bridge that gap for himself. In its attempts to envision the next piece of the puzzle, Western psychology could not have asked for a more appropriate influence.

Unlike the culture in which it originated, this new culture that the *dharma* is en-countering is a largely sedentary one. Increasingly we have come to realize, however, that real psychological and physical health do not exist separately from one another, but go hand in hand. One of the focuses of the new psychology, therefore, has been to rekindle the vitality and awareness of the body as a means of healing the pains and ills of the soul. This recognition of psychological and physical interdependence has spawned a wide variety of approaches and techniques which have been loosely joined together under the label *somatism*. The common denominator to all these different approaches is the body. Each approach, in its own way, focuses on a different aspect of embodiment in its attempt to engender peace of mind. In some cases the focus is the function of the breath; in other cases it is the structure of the body itself or the movement patterns that the body is able (or not able) to generate; and in others it is the denseness of the soft tissues of the body that keep emotion and energetic expression held or withheld. Taken together, each of these approaches forms an individual branch on the greater somatic tree. While each branch of a tree is unique, it is fundamentally linked to every other branch as well.

Many pioneers have contributed to the creation and nurturing of this tree. The late Ida P. Rolf (1896-1979) was one of them. Her chosen subject of inquiry was the structure and appearance of the body, and of its relationship to the gravitational field of the earth. In her insistence that well-being is to be discovered through the pursuance of that relationship alone, she would often be accused of attempting to depsychologize psychology. It was an accusation that probably pleased her. "It ain't psychology! It's only physiology!" she would roar. She kept on preaching the gospel of gravity throughout her life, serving as midwife to a form of therapeutic manipulation whose implications have only begun to be sorted out. Her vision became so well accepted within the field of somatic therapy that her surname became a verb.

The major somatic insights in this book are closely aligned with her vision and work. Not only is this the somatic tradition with which I am most intimately familiar; more significantly, it is the branch of the somatic tree that most strongly emphasizes the importance of creating a condition of balance within the structure of the body. As the title of this book implies, balance of body is one of the two major components on which the inquiry that we will be pursuing here is based. Balance of mind, the major focus and goal of Buddhist practice, is the other. What this book attempts to do is to illustrate how each of these aspects of balance is a factor in the establishment of the other. Pursuing one of these aspects alone, without the illumination that can be provided by the other, makes the task at hand much more difficult to achieve.

The current Western psychological model, with its roots in Viennese analysis, is not adequate to explain the experiences of a person whose body has attained heightened states of balance. The Buddhist psychological model describes that territory in depth and detail. As bodies change, people change. A body that becomes more structurally balanced may begin to experience itself, the world, and the relationship it bears to the world in a manner that is not at all consistent with its previous perceptions. It is as though we suddenly realize that some of the assumptions we have held to be inviolable no longer accurately describe the conditions of our lives. Notions of identity and relationship, of the distinction between our inner and outer worlds, and of corporeality and time—all of these may undergo alteration as the structure of the body begins to change. As bodies become more balanced, the rigidity of some of our attitudes and points of view falls away, just as does the tension that has kept us from that balance.

The difficulty we face in exploring heightened states of structural balance is that we may find ourselves traversing a terrain of psychological impressions not at all well traveled, let alone mapped and charted with any kind of accuracy. We simply do not have models capable of lending credence to these new impressions. Imagine for a moment what kind of reception you would probably get from the average person if you suggested that our notion of an "I," separate and distinct from the rest of existence, is but an illusory concept, a convenience rather than a fundamental truth. How would someone respond to your suggestion that the distinction we ordinarily draw between our inner and outer worlds is an arbitrary one at best that distorts, rather than reflects, actual experience? Yet perceptions like these may come to us in moments of heightened balance and ease. With some reluctance we are forced to admit that we can discard these perceptions only if we choose to discard the ease and lightness to which the condition of balance has also given rise. It is not possible to maintain the feeling tone of balance and ignore the shifts in perception that accompany it.

Just as the Buddhist psychological model is able to provide explanation for the perceptual shifts experienced by a person whose body is becoming more balanced, so too can the somatic model provide a foundation capable of reinvigorating Buddhist practices and teachings as they spread to the West. To a body that must struggle incessantly with the field of gravity, the insights and perspectives that these teachings suggest may seem like so much intellectual mind play. But to a body moving increasingly toward a condition of effortless support and balance, they will echo and confirm many of the impressions and states of mind that are becoming more commonplace. In the words of a contemporary Buddhist teacher, "Buddha is the center of gravity." To find the center of gravity within oneself, in other words to relate in an optimal way the energy field of the body with the gravitational field of the earth, is to encounter the essential experience to which the Buddha was trying to lead us. An understanding of this relationship will be of inestimable value to the Buddhist student as he or she explores the posture and process of sitting meditation.

All too often, the importance of the body and its relationship to the earth is overlooked in Buddhist practices. In spite of its professed allegiance to the indivisibility of experience and the fallacy of distinctions, Buddhist philosophy betrays, for the most part, as fundamental a somataphobic bias as does the Western philosophical tradition. The great majority of Buddhist schools focus primarily on mind as the arena of potential reward; body retains a much more diminished status as an avenue of exploration. Even though every nuance of mind is accompanied by a tactile sensation in the body, in most cases it is the element of mind that is pursued as an object of inquiry rather than the accompanying sensation.

This partiality in favor of the mechanics of the mind appears as an early development in Buddhist philosophy. In the literature of the *Abhidharma*, for example, the whole of reality is dissected and pared down into what are seen as its smallest constituent components, the overwhelming majority of which are portrayed as mental in nature. The later teachings of the *Yogacara* school, with its singular emphasis on the importance of mind, culminate in the doctrine of *Cittamatra*, the notion that mind alone matters. The danger with such a bias, no matter how profound, is that the practitioner may lose touch with the experience of body, without which there is no experience of mind, and of his relationship to the earth, without which there is no body.

Far from being a radical departure in the development of Buddhist philosophy, this acknowledgement of the importance of our relationship to the earth can be seen as a simple return to the beginning moments out of which the whole of that philosophy would eventually emerge. Shortly before his enlightenment, when the Buddha was questioned on whose authority he was claiming to be awakened, he simply smiled and lowered his hand to touch the earth. Through this gesture he implied that the earth itself was his witness and that he needed no other authority than this. In another even more germane interpretation of this story, it is said that the Buddha, in waging his final battle with the powers of doubt and delusion, called upon the power of the earth to aid him in his task. In affirming his connection with the earth (and with the power of gravity which establishes that connection), the Buddha was making a statement that has literal implications concerning the nature of the path and the teachings.

In the centuries following the Buddha's death, however, the importance of this connection appears, in large part, to have been either overlooked or forgotten. The simplicity of the original teachings would gradually become overshadowed by the increasingly intellectual nature of the philosophical systems that developed around the teachings. To embark on a Buddhist path became less and less a direct act of looking into one's own nature; it required, rather, the determination and ability to make one's way through a daunting array of intellectual commentaries and systems that were deemed essential to an understanding of what the Buddha had so simply set forth. One of the challenges facing the development and spread of Buddhist practice in the practical climate of North America is to bring itself back down to earth, to make itself once again accessible to the larger mass of humanity for whom the teachings were originally intended. It is my sincere hope that this book will serve to help clarify and simplify these teachings, rather than to obscure them underneath the shroud of yet another enigmatic system.

To organize the material effectively, I have found it necessary to divide this book into two sections. The main body of the text is to be found in the first section. Here the major ideas concerning the mechanics and implications of balance are presented. The second section reiterates and enlarges upon many of these basic issues and ideas in the form of practical exercises, and the reader is encouraged to experiment with them. While these two sections will serve to clarify each other, some familiarization with the information in the first section will be helpful before embarking on the exploration outlined in the second.

A final note: One word will appear again and again throughout this book, and that word is *experience*. The shift in perception that a balanced body and mind promote takes us from the lukewarm remove of concepts and plants us squarely into the intensely vibrant world of immediate sensory experience. To this end I have attempted to limit my observations to events and modes of perception that I have personally experienced and to forgo the temptation to become sidetracked on every speculative detour that appeared along the way. The vision in which this book culminates is directly dependent on our ability to appreciate the nature of this shift toward experience, away from concept and interpretation. The view of the world it suggests is a radically different one from our conventional world view, and yet it is every bit as logical as the view it is meant to augment. I cautiously use the word "augment" here, rather than "replace," as I am clear that in our discussions of these differing points of view it is not a question of one being any better or more or less accurate than the other. Both, in their way, present a coherent picture of the world based on the nature of the data that each has gathered. Both are of value in our movement through life. The point is simply that our ability to embrace and relate to the world from this new vantage point of experience brings with it a significant lessening of our condition of suffering.

PART I:
The Conditions of Balance

Balance of Body, Balance of Mind

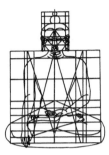

*B*alance is a condition in which the interplay of separate forces has arrived at a state of perfect equilibrium. It is always a function of relationship, dependent upon the interaction of at least two components whose relative strengths and presence counteract each other so that neither retains a position of dominance. Sometimes balance can be precisely measured in terms of weight or quantity. One hundred pounds of grain, for example, can be accurately determined on a scale down to the single kernel. At other times, balance is an entirely subjective matter, as is the case with the shapes and colors that a painter applies to a canvas. The balance that our body and mind can attain is partially quantifiable and partially a matter of a highly personal monitoring of sensations and feelings. While there are certain signs that indicate that a true balance of body and balance of mind have been achieved, they are not ultimately measurable. The reason for this is that, when applied to the condition of our body and mind, balance never remains static, as it does with grain on a scale. It refers, rather, to a dynamic process that changes constantly and manifests in degrees. What appears as balanced one moment may not be the next.

Balance of body is a function of the relationship between the physical structure of the body and the gravitational field of the earth. The outer signs of a balanced body are alignment, symmetry, and resilience. When standing, a balanced body appears organized around a vertical axis or line that runs from the top of the head to the bottom of the feet. The left and right sides of the body are symmetrically arranged around this line. The front and back of the body mirror each other with an integrity that minimizes shifts in space away from the vertical axis. A balanced body moves with resilience and ease. All the individual parts of the body work together as a coordinated and synergetic whole. Most importantly, a balanced body does not have to hold itself erect; like a tall skyscraper or tree, it achieves its erectness by virtue of its structure and maintains its erectness by virtue of its resilience. A balanced body possesses a feeling of energetic flow as though a river of tactile sensations were moving freely throughout its length.

Balance of mind is a function of the relationship between the mental faculty of perception and the objects and events that appear in our sensory fields. A balanced mind possesses many of the same attributes as a balanced body. A balanced mind aligns itself around the same vertical axis as does a balanced body. Residing in this way in the approximate center of the body, the mind is able to maintain a balance between the internal workings of perception and cognition and the external pulls of the sensory objects with which it must constantly interact. Such a mind is neither grossly introverted nor extroverted. It does not lose its center by being drawn out by the sensory fields that continually beckon; nor does it have to protect itself from these fields by retreating into itself. This state of mental balance is further mirrored in the ability of the brain to function symmetrically. The brain is composed of a right and left hemisphere; each is responsible for separate and distinct functions. A balanced mind moves freely back and forth between the two hemispherical bases according to the situation in which it finds itself. Not restricted to patterns of behavior that favor one side of the brain over the other, a balanced mind is able to respond in a rational, outgoing way at one moment and in a more sensual, introspective way the next. Finally, and again most importantly, a balanced mind is remarkably fluid and resilient. It too does not need to hold on to anything, be it a visual or auditory event in the world outside the body or a thought or emotion that is generated internally. The mind enters into a condition of holding by reacting to these objects or events with clinging or aversion. Through either reaction the fluidity, resilience, and ultimate balance of the mind are forfeited.

Imbalance in the physical structure of the body causes pain and tension as the body struggles to remain erect. An imbalanced body has an overall appearance of rigidity or flaccidity (often in combination), a feeling of numbness or discomfort. An imbalanced mind is severely limited and constricted. While a balanced mind is inherently spacious and multidimensional, the activity of an imbalanced mind will be largely restricted to its superficial dimensions. Such activity often manifests as a seldom interrupted inner monologue that effectively blocks out any access to the mind's deeper reaches. An imbalanced mind experiences little stability, but is instead pulled and drawn this way and that by the ongoing tug of sensory objects. It is, finally, dominated by an unrelenting sense of "I" which functions as a filter that colors and assesses everything the mind can receive. This filter causes us to view the world from a literally single-minded perspective. By distorting and limiting much of the data that enters the mind, such narrowing of perception has great potential to cause suffering.

One of the central premises of this book is that balances and imbalances at a physical level in the body are directly reflected in equivalent balances and imbalances at internal levels of the mind. Bring the body to balance, and the mind follows naturally. Bring the mind to balance, and the physical structure of the body must inevitably respond and shift. A condition of imbalance in the structure of the body severely interferes with the mind's ability to realize its most open, expansive nature.

Neurotic patterns of mind, in turn, create structural patterns of blockage and distortion in the body.

By probing ever more deeply into the nature of balance, we can begin to examine how these two aspects of experience, body and mind, are able to influence each other. While it is helpful in the beginning to approach the issues of body and mind in the most conventional manner, as though they were separate aspects of experience having little in common, gradually we will see that the components of body and mind share a common ground that emphasizes their similarity rather than their differences. Ultimately, this realization will be the most direct reward of balance. In many spiritual traditions the synchronization of body and mind is the precondition that allows the student entrance into what is termed the "ground of being." It is intriguing that this aspect of experience is labeled in this way, as it is to the "ground" itself that we must first turn our attention.

The Two Faces of Gravity

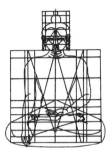

"As one falls to the ground, one must lift oneself by aid of the ground."
Kularnava Tantra

G ravity is one of the most predominant forces in the universe. An inherent property of every particle of matter, gravity draws objects to each other according to their mass, with smaller objects inevitably coming under the influence of larger ones. In this way it orchestrates the course of planets as they move in an orderly fashion around the sun and establishes our primary destiny as an earth-bound species. Scientists who embrace the theory of the "Big Bang" as the most likely explanation of how the universe began speculate that the force of gravity came into existence an unfathomably small microsecond after that event occurred and has remained constant throughout the universe ever since.

Our practical experience of gravity comes from the sense of being almost inextricably connected to the ground directly underneath our bodies. We have become so accustomed to this sensation, however, that we take it for granted. When we climb or descend a steep hill we become momentarily more appreciative of the magnitude of this force. Most of the time, though, we remain blind to its presence. Much like the oxygen that fills our air, it is an invisible factor in our lives.

Our physical relationship with gravity determines whether our journey through life will be one of buoyancy and lightness or tension and struggle. To encourage structural balance, we need to align the energy field of the human body with the gravitational field of the earth so that they are able to relate to each other in a mutually supportive manner. If our bodies can assume the structural coordinates that allow for this relationship, then we become balanced, and we reap a sense of well-being as a natural and inevitable consequence. If we are unable to do so, then the experience of well-being becomes maddeningly elusive.

What we are dealing with here are two distinct, yet obviously interrelated, notions of energy. Our practical understanding of gravity is still largely based on the Newtonian conception of energy as a force whose expression and influence are so consistent and unvarying that we can measure it with mathematical precision. Such mathematical exactness allows us to deduce an underlying law or principle, and Newton's observation that energy varies with the square of the distance from the source has proven to be both accurate and dependable. Nowhere can the operation of this law be seen so clearly as in the space program. The rocket engines must initially exert an enormous thrust capable of freeing the spacecraft from the hold that the gravitational field has on it. Finally, after the spacecraft has traveled a great distance, the gravitational force of the earth diminishes to a point where our astronauts are able to experience the phenomenon of weightlessness.

Gravitational energy conforms in all observable respects to Newton's predictions for its behavior. It is highly ordered and unfailingly consistent. Gravitational energy fluctuates only to the extent that an object is capable of altering the distance that exists between itself and the source of the gravity. For all practical purposes this is impossible for us as human beings. We are born on the outermost layer of the earth's surface, pass our life on this surface, and die here. Gravity is the most constant force affecting our lives.[1]

The second notion of energy deals with what might be called "vital" energy. This is the energy of life, which in some manifestation or another, is characteristic of all living organisms. This nonmechanistic notion has nothing to do with distance and even less to do with constancy. It is characterized by pulsation, wildly differing periods of fluctuation which are not reducible to prediction, and sensations of streaming and flow. While it is present during the entire life of every living organism, it may manifest in a disordered electromotive pattern of low overall voltage, or it may appear as a wonderfully organized and coherent force of great magnetism and influence.

One of the major factors in determining how this vital energy will, in fact, present itself is the relationship that exists between the living organism and the gravitational field which acts on it. We cannot change the gravitational field, but we can alter

---

1) The force of gravity is one of the major cornerstones of classical physics. As a theory, it has behaved flawlessly for hundreds of years in its ability to predict and explain the behavior of physical events whose size and scale are within the comprehension of human beings. The limitations to this theory have only surfaced in the twentieth century as scientists have begun to turn their attention to the behavior of situations that are not at all related to the scale of personal experience but are, rather, either infinitesimally large or small. While Einstein's conception of a space-time continuum neatly dispenses with the classical notion of gravitational force in its explanation of how the universe is held together, it has little practical applicability to our day-to-day existence as inhabitants of this planet. For us, and for most objects and events whose size is comprehensible by us, Newton's conception of gravitational attraction still holds steadfastly true. Einstein may have proved that, in the way we conventionally envision it, there is no such thing as the "force of gravity." However, the fact remains that when the apple is tossed into the air, it unfailingly returns to the earth. So also do our bodies, depending upon their physical structure, experience different sensations that can be understood and explained only in terms of our classical conception of gravity.

our relationship to this field. If we can change our position so it is more in line and more in harmony with gravitational energy, then our tendency to randomness, disorder, and deterioration will decrease. Put more simply, the quality of energy that is available to a human being depends on his ability to come to balance.

Gravity, then, is simply a neutral force. Only our relationship with gravity determines whether we experience it in a constructive or destructive way. Depending on the structure of the body on which it acts, gravity can either support us and provide a springboard for our activities or it can pull at us and tear us down. Gravity affects us in a positive, supportive way when all the major segments of our body come into vertical alignment in a completely relaxed and balanced manner. Just as successive floors in a skyscraper are stacked directly on top of one another, each bodily segment must be able to rest effortlessly on the segment immediately beneath it, which in turn functions as its support. Seen from the side, the head will appear to rest directly on top of the neck, which is supported by the shoulder girdle and thorax all the way down through the abdomen, pelvis, upper and lower legs, ankles, and feet.

The contact between the bottoms of the feet and the earth is critical. The surface of the earth functions as the bottommost segment of the human body, our final and lowest limb. At this point of contact, the message of the body's balance or imbalance is communicated directly to the earth. Our relationship to this point "underneath our standing" has great bearing on our ability to develop wisdom or "understanding" in our life. By familiarizing ourselves with the ground on which we stand, understanding can arise. The more we understand about ourselves, in turn, the closer we come to gaining access to the "ground of being" that was mentioned at the end of the previous chapter.

Access to understanding is dependent on whether or not a body need exert any unnecessary muscular effort to remain erect. It is easy to see what happens when the structure of the body begins to lose its verticality. Consider, for instance, the placement of the head. In proper alignment and with proper support, it can sit effortlessly on top of the body like a balanced crown. It is shielded from the pull of gravity by the mass of the body supporting it. If the head is too far forward relative to the ideal vertical, however, it presents a whole new area for gravity to act upon. In this case the muscles in the back of the neck must contract to offset this force. If they did not, the head would fall down onto the chest.

This condition is true of any deviation from ideal vertical posture, wherever it occurs in the body. The deviation may appear in the lack of balance between any portion of the right and left sides of the body, the front and back of the body (as in the example of the head and neck), or even between the outermost tissues of the body and the deeper core structures. Given any of these situations, gravity suddenly becomes a menacing force against which we must work to keep ourselves erect. When this conflict is resolved, gravity becomes a highly benevolent support that allows us to remain erect without having to exert any effort at all.

One of the simplest examples of this phenomenon can be demonstrated by trying to balance a kitchen broom upside down on a finger. There is a point when the broom becomes completely vertical and, top-heavy though it may be, seems to balance with effortless poise in midair. As soon as the broom begins to wander away from this perfect verticality, the finger supporting it must quickly be shifted to prevent it from falling to the floor.

A valid question remains as to how the earth's gravity, which by its very nature draws smaller objects on or near its surface to itself, can be responsible for offering not only support, but the experience of buoyancy as well. People whose bodily structure is able to shift in the direction of greater balance, relaxation, and verticality often report that the experience of gravity seems to reverse itself. No longer does the body feel as if it is being pulled only in the direction of the earth. Instead, there is a physical sensation that the body, without any muscular effort, is being lifted upward as though it is being drawn to another as yet undiscovered force, which is analogous to the earth's gravity, yet opposite to it in the direction of its pull. How can this phenomenon be explained?

We must keep in mind that what we are dealing with is the intermingling of two highly different manifestations of energy — one inanimate and the other animate. As human beings we exist much like seeds and are metaphorically subject to the same influences and experiences that condition and characterize the life of a seed. If a seed is thrown onto fertile soil and nurtured with adequate moisture, clean air, and the heat of the sun, it will sprout into the stem of a plant or a flower. As its delicate green shoot rises upward, as though reaching out toward the sun, its roots grow larger and stronger as they sink deeper in an ever more intricate webbing into the earth. However, if the same seed falls upon inadequate soil and is unable to receive a proper amount of moisture and heat, it withers and decays back into the ground on which it fell.

Our journey through life is much like that of a seed in search of the conditions that will insure its growth and flowering. As humans we have many of the same requirements as the seed: clean water and air, healthful nutrients, and exposure to the sun. But unlike the seed, we have the ability to move along the surface of the earth. We needn't root ourselves in any one place. Our food comes from the earth, but not from the earth directly beneath our feet. The nourishment that we receive from the ground underneath our feet comes from the gravitational field itself, for it is our relationship with this field that supports a physical sense of well-being in a balanced body.

A balanced and relaxed body can surrender its physical weight to the pull of gravity and still remain standing. This is not possible for an imbalanced body, which must hold its weight up and away from the pull of gravity. If it were to surrender its weight to gravity, it would fall to the ground. By holding itself up and not allowing its weight to drop through the body, however, it exists much like a seed that was sown on a rock and is not able to contact the soil and begin its growth. That seed will die without having experienced the fulfillment of flowering.

When we allow our weight to drop downward into the earth, we establish roots, much like the seedling. We begin to grow and mature. At some point a mysterious phenomenon begins to occur. Our vital energy begins to flower, and while we experience ourselves as fully rooted in the earth, we can also begin to feel a force pulling us upward. The body begins to grow freely, and our sense of being is transformed. At this point we are no longer seeds. We have flowered into a whole new dimension of experience.

To arrive at this point is our birthright as inhabitants of this planet. It is the natural fulfillment of our destiny as human "seeds." Of course, there are no guarantees of success, and a quick look around at the conditions of life on our planet today would suggest that our current crop is not nearly so full and bountiful as it might be. Nevertheless, we appear to be acquiring a growing awareness of our condition and the choices open to us. In our increasing understanding of the healing power that the field of gravity can offer us, we can more actively participate in determining whether we plant ourselves in fertile ground or not. By pursuing the mystery of our relationship with gravity, we can embark on a journey that leads to fulfillment.

Suffering and its Causes

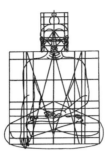

*T*wenty-five hundred years ago a young Indian prince left his home and family to venture alone out into the world. It must not have been an easy decision for him to make. He had been born into a wealthy noble family and had been raised with all the comforts and privileges of the court. He was being groomed to succeed his father one day as ruler of the kingdom. He had a wife and son. His future, as we would say, looked exceedingly bright. Underneath the intoxicating prospects for the likely course that his life would follow, however, a growing dissatisfaction had begun to appear. He was a prince, a special person, different from the subjects he was destined to govern. Yet he also realized that there was no difference. The circumstances of his birth would not be sufficient to protect him from falling ill, from growing old, from experiencing disappointment and loss, and, in the end, from dying. Somehow, somewhere, he knew there must exist an antidote to the pain caused by these perplexing dilemmas, and he was determined to find it. He left his life of comfort and security and embarked on an extraordinary journey of self-exploration in which alternating episodes of extreme deprivation and ecstatic insight would ultimately give way, many years later, to a profound state of balance. Within this condition the former prince, Siddhartha Gotama, found the antidote he had been looking for. He became enlightened and was henceforth known as the Buddha, a title reserved for a person who has awakened from the dreams and illusions that are responsible for so much of the pain and confusion we feel in our lives.

After the Buddha experienced his enlightenment, he began moving across India, speaking freely with people wherever he went. He spoke of what had happened to him, of the deep transformation that had taken place in his life, and of the sense of relief and contentment that accompanied it. He pointed out that his experience was not unique, that it was potentially available to anyone, and he stressed that the path leading to this experience provided the only context capable of creating satisfaction.

He also spoke honestly of what he saw. Just as a mirror reflects whatever is brought before it with complete impartiality, he shared with people his honest observation of the condition of their lives. He had known what it felt like to live as a human seed and now understood the fulfillment of a flower in bloom. He could see that the frustrations and pain of human life were the result of our interference with the natural process of blossoming and awakening. He talked of the reasons behind this interference and explained why it seemed to occur with such frequency and regularity. Finally, he offered suggestions on how one could initiate this process for oneself and transform one's own experience into the experience of a Buddha. The essence of his teaching is summed up in a handful of simple statements which form the nucleus of the psychological model that we will be exploring in this book. They have come to be known, down through the centuries, as the *Four Noble Truths.*

The first truth the Buddha shares with us reflects his observation on the quality of life. He saw that the condition that most universally dominates and defines our experience of life is that of pain and suffering. For the average person, to live is to suffer. We may wish to believe otherwise or even erect elaborate psychological barriers to shield ourselves from this truth. This is, at best, a harsh and confronting idea to accept, but masking truth does not erase it. Deep within us, far beneath the superficial level of consciousness with which we mostly identify, lives the recognition of this simple truth: to be alive is to experience pain. The voice of pain has many volumes and tones. Sometimes it appears as a faint echo, a whisper that we are able to ignore or dismiss. At other times it becomes strident and unrelenting. Like a thunder cloud that covers the sun, pain rarely allows any warmth or comfort to shine through.

An honest look around should rapidly convince us of this truth. Currently, untold millions of people are confronted with famine or lack of adequate medical supplies. The very environment that nourishes and supports us can turn menacing in a moment and destroy us. Throughout our recorded history, countless numbers of people have been forced to take part in fruitless wars; even more have suffered because of it. Countless others have been ruthlessly persecuted for their beliefs.

Such extreme forms of human suffering may seem remote to many of us who have been fortunate enough never to have experienced them directly. Buddhist thought, however, directs our attention to the cycle of life itself as evidence of this truth. All of us, fortunate or not, are subject to the same conditions of birth, decay, and death. We cannot escape the pains that accompany our birth into this world, the illnesses and disappointments that we encounter along the way, the inevitable decay that accompanies the process of aging, and our ultimate dissolution at the moment of death.

While we have seen advances that seem to make our lives more comfortable and less of a struggle, our modern world has also brought with it an incredible array of forms of dissatisfaction that many more primitive peoples could never have even envisioned. Our increased mobility and leisure bring with them the opportunity to reflect on the fact that something is missing from our lives, that some essential ingredient has been overlooked or left out altogether. Even though we may achieve certain signs of success, we are often left with the nagging feeling that somehow something is still not quite right. We imagine that if certain things could be different, then everything would be fine. So we struggle to alter the conditions that we think are keeping us from attaining happiness, and the result is that a new set of conditions turn out to be just as unsatisfactory as the ones they replaced. This lack of genuine contentment is the focus of the Buddha's inquiry.

In the second truth, the Buddha proposes that the cause of suffering can be directly traced to the difficulty we have in accepting reality exactly as it is. The suffering we experience is a direct result of desire.

Desire has many faces. It may range from the simple wish to change points of mild irritation to the seemingly uncontrollable urges that precede the most passionate or violent acts. In all its different forms and degrees, desire is motivated by our attachment to pleasure and our aversion to pain. If we are ill, we want to be well. If we are well, we want to experience something even more pleasurable or exciting. Our mind views pleasure and pain in the light of our ability or inability to attain various possessions, achievements, or recognitions. Many of us, for example, have highly ambitious goals that we strive to fulfill. If we fail to achieve these goals, we experience pain and frustration. If we are able to achieve them, we may experience a momentary pleasure. But then what often develops is an attachment to what we have achieved or created. Instead of a lasting satisfaction with our accomplishment, what arises is the fear of its loss or, even worse, the gnawing realization that in spite of the achievement there is still no real contentment. By constantly desiring more and more, we move further and further away from a true knowledge of ourselves until death comes, and--within the transmigratory vision of Buddhism--we begin the process anew, round after round of birth and death, round after round of suffering. Desire, then, is a force that moves us in a direction directly opposite to the one that might lead us to real contentment.

Attachment, clinging, and aversion are all aspects of desire. Any of these actions dams up the flow of life and diminishes our vitality. We may have a highly significant and enriching experience, but if we cling to it and strive to retain the object or feeling of the experience exactly as we first encountered it, we sink further into the bondage from which the experience may have initially offered release. Ultimately experiences are "just" experiences. By clinging to some and avoiding others, life ceases to be a cooperative adventure of growing to fruition and instead becomes a constant struggle.

The Buddha further points out how our lives are conditioned by erroneous views and beliefs to which we are deeply attached. Truth knows no distinctions. Yet we are certain that the very fact of our existence is dependent on such things as our thoughts, feelings, age, sex, race, social position, our religious, national, and political views. We take our points of view so seriously that we distort our ability to see things as they are. We lose our true sense of grounding and instead accept as real and meaningful the airy vision that our imagination has constructed.

Perhaps the most difficult notion for us to let go of is our belief in the existence of a self, an "I," a central, unchanging focal point which runs the show of life and to which all experience is referred. So deep-seated is this belief, that it may never even occur to us to question it at all. The Buddha's teaching, however, calls for a complete re-examination of every aspect of our lives, and the process demands that we distinguish very clearly and carefully between reality and our beliefs about reality. The Buddha looked and looked, and in the end he could not find even a trace of evidence that anything like a self existed in him. For the Buddha it must have been a moment of great relief and liberation. Certainly, as he looked inside, he found many things -- a whole host of thoughts, emotions, feelings, and sensations, all of them constantly changing. But as he kept observing, he noticed that none of them really seemed to belong to him. They would emerge into his awareness out of nowhere, linger for a period of time, and then disappear. The more he looked, the more he came to understand that all of the psychophysical phenomena with which we normally identify and consequently take as evidence of our existence as separate, individual beings, is just a passing show.

We are so attached to the importance of our individualized existence that the suggestion that this belief might be the result of a fundamental misperception is seriously threatening. Oblivious to the truth, however, we continue our journey through life with a distorted vision of how things are, and pain and suffering become inevitable. Our attachment to erroneous beliefs insures that our lives don't work.

The Third Noble Truth is the Buddha's assurance to us that there exists a way out of our dilemma. While it is true that the fundamental undercurrent of human life (given our inclination to desire and attachment) is one of suffering and pain, it is also true that a state of contentment and balance does exist and is, in fact, possible for us to attain. Such a state is free from the continuous actions of clinging and aversion and the subsequent pain and disorientation to which they give rise. It is marked by an honest acceptance of life and the constantly changing situations that life offers. It allows us to understand that nothing whatso-ever could be added to or subtracted from the conditions of the present moment to make it any more perfect than it already is. Perfection, in this sense, does not refer to an extraordinary state that may or may not be attainable. It refers instead to what is real right now, extraordinary or ordinary as it may appear. Learning to view our present circumstances as perfect enables us to short-circuit the force of desire which so greatly interferes with our ability to accept things as they are. Only an attitude of acceptance enables us to open to all the sensory components in a given situation. As we shall see later, this attitude, coupled with our ability to perceive these components clearly, is the doorway through which we can find relief from the suffering that troubles us.

The Buddha's great gift to the people of his time was that he shared his enlightenment with them. It is recorded that he originally did not intend to because he feared that no one would understand what he was trying to say. The truths he had uncovered were simple and evident, and yet they represented a radical departure from the belief systems of the times. Ultimately, however, he was moved to share what he had learned, and for the duration of his life he traveled throughout India, dispensing the teaching freely wherever he went. He, himself, was the best evidence of the truth of his teaching. He was able to say, "Look at what has happened to me, and know that if it is possible for me, then it is possible for you as well." In accepting the truth about himself, the Buddha was able to transcend the condition of suffering. The forces of desire had dropped away.

In the Fourth, and final, Noble Truth the Buddha indicates how we might come to experience real contentment and balance within ourselves. The sequence of instructions that he outlined is known as the "Noble Eightfold Path," and it is the Buddha's prescription for alleviating suffering. In it he cautions us about the perils that undermine our efforts and suggests attitudes that can support us in our aim. The dual cultivation of acceptance and awareness is fundamental to this path. The form of meditation that the Buddha discovered is based on these two attitudes, and they will provide an underlying theme throughout the course of this book.

The cause of pain, the possibility of its cessation, and the way to stop it — this is what the Buddha taught. Time and again people would try to engage him in discussions of a metaphysical nature. Time and again he would politely decline. Such matters, he would say, are ultimately of little significance. What is important is the recognition that there is pain, and there is a way out of pain. His message is simple, direct, and clear. Taken to heart, it has provided guidance to countless spiritual travelers down through the centuries, even unto the present day.

How different this explanation of suffering and its causes is from the current Western model. To a sophisticated Westerner, it may at first appear simplistic. Even worse, it could be argued, such an attitude would encourage people to do nothing at all and become more entrenched in whatever problems they encounter. The Buddhist psychological model, however, does not condone inaction. It encourages us to become aware of a situation, to accept it as it is, and then allow our body to respond in whatever fashion is natural. Our Western model on the other hand would have us change, change, and then change some more. In some situations this Western strategy is unquestionably effective, but it has its limitations as well. If we keep on attempting to change everything that we find unsatisfactory, we ultimately end up feeding the source of suffering articulated by the Buddha. The applicability of the Buddhist strategy may become clearer if we now turn our attention back to the problem of the body and its relationship to gravity.

Pain

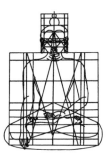

*O*ur relationship with gravity provides a meaningful context within which to explore the truth of suffering. The experience of a body that is not in balance within the gravitational field will be primarily one of discomfort and pain. An imbalanced body cannot be supported by gravity, but must produce its own support by itself. It does this by constantly tensing specific muscle groups to offset what it feels as the destructive, downward pull of gravity. While such a strategy may work satisfactorily in the beginning, over an extended period of time we are left exhausted from the effort. Life slowly ceases to be an uplifting adventure and instead becomes a subtle, but constant, struggle simply to remain erect. The severity of the struggle parallels the severity of the imbalance. The possibility of ease slips further and further away, and our lives increasingly take on the flavor of frustration, fatigue, and disorientation. To lose one's balance is to initiate an insidious chain of reactive events.

It may be hard to believe that such a simple thing as imbalance can have so potentially devastating an effect, but consider the odds that we create when gravity becomes our opponent. The energy of the earth's gravitational field is limitless from our point of view. The amount of force that a human being can exert is inconsequential in comparison. To pit these two forces against each other amounts to a preposterous mismatch.

Ordinary rest is no longer able to bring an imbalanced body relief, because the fascia ensheathing those muscles that must work so hard to counteract the effect of gravity gradually forfeits its extensibility and resilience. Fascia is one of the most widespread tissues in the body and plays a significant role in the creation and alleviation of pain. It performs a variety of functions, the most noteworthy of which is to provide an enveloping covering or sheath surrounding muscle tissue. The relationship between a cylinder and a piston in an automobile engine roughly corresponds to the relationship between fascia and muscle in the human body. The major property of muscle tissue is its ability to contract and expand. The major property of fascia is its remarkable resilience, which allows it to conform its shape to the contractile phase of the muscle it ensheathes. As a muscle contracts, the fascia shortens to accommodate the contraction. As the muscle releases its contraction, the fascia lengthens, and it allows the muscle to assume once again its most fully relaxed span.

The interplay between these two tissues works wonderfully as long as muscular tissue is free to expand and contract at will. To maintain its resilience, the fascia needs to be continually exercised. A balanced body receives this exercise through the natural movements that occur during the course of an active day. We begin to get into trouble, however, as soon as the structure of the body begins to stray from an optimally balanced alignment. In an imbalanced body, certain muscle groups must become chronically contracted, their antagonists chronically elongated, in order to provide support for the body and prevent it from succumbing to the pull of gravity and falling over. If a muscle remains chronically held in either of its contractile phases for a long enough period of time, the fascia that surrounds it will not be able to receive the exercise it requires. Instead, it will conform to the shape of the muscle and gradually begin to harden around it, effectively forfeiting its resilience.

Thankfully, fascia is a remarkably plastic tissue. Just as it can lose its resilience, so too can it regain it. Through the application of force, the biochemical composition of fascial tissue can be influenced and its shape ultimately altered. The field of gravity applies just such a force to the fascial tissue of the body throughout our entire lives. Depending on whether the structure of the body is primarily balanced or imbalanced within this field, this force will be experienced in a supportive or degenerative way. A Rolfer's hands are also capable of applying the force necessary to restore fascial resilience and, furthermore, to coax a body into a configuration that can offset the potentially degenerative effect of gravity.

The plasticity of the body's fascia, much like the force of gravity that acts on it, is a neutral phenomenon that can work for us or against us. With conscious intention and direct manipulation we may influence our body to assume a structure that gravity will naturally support. However, in the picture of imbalance we are presenting here, it is the plasticity of the fascia that carries out the sentence to which our imbalance has condemned us. As the fascia surrounding a chronically contracted muscle slowly loses its gelatinous resilience and becomes hardened, it leaves no choice for that muscle but to maintain its condition of contraction. Now even if the muscle wanted to relax its tension, as when the body assumes a position of rest, it would be unable to do so completely. Furthermore, such deteriorated and contracted fascia inhibits the ability of the dense network of capillaries and nerve fibers that pass through it to perform their functions. The result is not only pain and fatigue resulting from chronic muscular holding, but also the gradual loss of health and vitality that accompanies the restriction to our circulatory and nervous systems.

The condition of a body's fascia, then, reveals a great deal about the emotional and physical status of the person. Just as the respiratory cycle is necessary for life to continue, the ability of muscle tissue to engage freely in its constant play of contraction and release is necessary for health and vitality. Appropriate muscular activity functions like a pump to assist in the all-important circulation of bodily fluids and helps us exchange our personal energy with the greater environment in which we live. If this lesser acknowledged flow of vital circulation becomes impaired, we tend to become stagnant and withdraw from life. When muscle tissue loses its ability to contract and release at will, the body suffers.

Our emotional sufferings are directly related to our physical ones. Anger, fear, excitement, depression — all of these are expressed through the tensing and relaxation of specific muscle groups in the body. The emotion and its physical expression coexist with each other. It is not a matter of one causing the other; they either happen simultaneously or not at all. If a major period of a person's life is strongly conditioned by any one of these powerful emotions, then the fascia surrounding the muscles involved in the expression of the emotion will become hardened in response to the long-term muscular pattern of contraction or release.

The gradual loss of fascial resilience, then, may be a reflection not just of physical imbalance; it may also be the result of the hold a predominant emotional pattern has on a body. In the first case one's imbalance and subsequent struggle with gravity become frozen in the body. In the second the predominant emotion becomes a permanent fixture in the person's life. The emotion appears in the person's customary manner of expression and way of relating to the world, and assures its own continuation by taking form in the flesh of the body. The situation becomes more complex over time, as these two underlying causes of bodily holding begin to influence each other. Holding that is largely emotional in origin will begin to interfere with balance, while holding that is more a function of simple physical imbalance can make a person much more prone to disturbing emotional patterns.

An emotional expression that crystallizes in the tissue of the body leaves a person little choice but to relate to life through the bias of that emotion. A body tied up in such a dominant emotional expression is no longer free to respond openly to the full range of life's offerings. Instead, everything must first be filtered through the prevailing emotional overlay. It is a little like wearing colored glasses to view the world. If worn so long that their presence is forgotten, one may come to wonder why the world seems to have a singular tint to it. Such distorted vision can be particularly treacherous in that one's experience of the world will often appear to justify the distorted view. For example, a body that is locked in an expression of anger or fear will keep on encountering over and over again what it perceives as situations about which to be angry or fearful.

The basis for much of our intellectual pain is a gnawing feeling of being unrelated to a universe that, through advances in our scientific understanding, has grown almost unfathomably large. We live in an age that has no clear cosmological vision of union and order. On the contrary, every new scientific discovery seems to elaborate on a picture of the universe that is increasingly random and perplexing. Where conceivably do we fit in to all this?

In the Ptolemaic system, which dominated Western thought until the sixteenth century, our planet — and, by extension, ourselves — existed at the very hub of the universe. We were the center around which the universal drama revolved. With Copernicus' observation, and Galileo's subsequent demonstration, that the sun — not the earth — is the center of our solar system, the security born of such a self-absorbed notion was destroyed. Of course physical pain caused by a body's imbalance within the gravitational field was as much a reality five hundred years ago as it is today. Gravity did not have to be "discovered" before it could affect us. But at least the Copernican cosmology supported a notion of a God who could provide encouragement and consolation in the face of pain. Within an arena of quasars, black holes, and distances measured in light years, our sense of center falls further apart, and our old gods don't seem to have a chance. Ours is a universe that cannot be comprehended; our place in it is even more problematic.

To be at odds with one's place in the universe is to live in great pain. To regain our sense of connection, however, we need not concern ourselves with the vastness of which our scientific inquiry has made us so acutely aware. The key is much closer to home. Our place in the universe is determined by the gravitational field of our planet. We are Earthlings, embryonic beings connected through the umbilical cord of gravity to Mother Earth. This is our given place in the universe, our rightful place; to function with complete ease and comfort in the gravitational field is to experience an appropriate connection to the whole cosmos. Gravity, then, is at once the source of much of our pain as well as the key to its dissolution. To arrive at such a dissolution, however, we must begin with what we can most immediately experience. We must begin with the awareness of our pain.

Our most common response to pain is to attempt to alleviate it. We consider it to be intrusive, a personal violation of our right to happiness, and so we inevitably try to make it go away. If it appears as a predominantly physical sensation, we may try to disguise it with drugs or seek the help of professionals trained in techniques designed to minimize or relieve pain. If it appears in a predominantly emotional form, the result perhaps of a shocking disappointment or loss, we may attempt to manipulate the external circumstances that we perhaps perceive as being responsible for the pain. Unable to alter the course of events, we may find ourselves turning to a close friend or professional for consolation and solace, hoping beyond hope that the pain will only go away. We are so adverse to the idea of accepting our pain, that if these strategies don't seem to work, we will usually attempt to block pain from our awareness — an action much like sweeping dirt under a rug. Miraculously, this often seems to work and, in the beginning at least, is one of the most effective ways for us to "get rid of" pain. The price we pay for this, however, is high. While it may initially succeed in diminishing the awareness of our pain, in the long run it also greatly diminishes our vitality.

The mechanism we use to block pain (or, for that matter, any bodily sensation) from our awareness is muscular contraction. Most of us are familiar with how the major muscles in our body work and with the primary function they perform. Their systematic contraction and relaxation allow us to move through space. While this is true of the large outer layer of muscles, a whole other function is performed by an underlying layer of small and delicate muscles. They are mostly found deep at the joints of the skeleton and are the fine tuners of the body. While the large muscles perform the major obvious movements, the small muscles refine that movement into a graceful and fluid motion. The large muscles move us from place to place, while the small muscles provide us with balance.

If a large muscle succumbs to a condition of chronic contraction, our range of movement becomes limited. If a smaller muscle becomes chronically contracted, we lose our ability to perform the subtle adjustments of balance, and our movement becomes stiff. Our bodies lack the graceful appearance of coordination. In reality it is impossible to separate the functions of these outer and inner layers of muscle. They work in cooperation with each other, and any interference to one of these layers will immediately affect the other. Even so, we can say that it is primarily by tensing the smaller intrinsic muscles that we are able to block out the presence of pain.

In doing so, we significantly interfere with our body's ability to perform the refined and subtle movements so necessary to maintain balance. Such holding and freezing of deep muscular tissue eventually gives rise to a condition of numbness. While it may be true that there is no pain, there is no real feeling of life or vitality either. The situation is similar to what happens when you apply ice to a part of your body. If ice is placed on a finger, you can numb it sufficiently to be able to prick yourself with a needle without experiencing any pain. By blocking out the awareness of pain, we become numb to life, and our body begins to stagnate.

A chronic contraction of muscular tissue dams up the flow of vital energy in much the same way as a knotted and tangled hose limits the amount of water capable of flowing through it. The force of the water will remain the same whether the hose is knotted or not. But in the case of a knotted hose, a great deal of pressure will build at the places where the flow is impeded. Over a long enough period of time, the hose may break. Our bodies are the physical manifestation of the mysterious energy of life. While a hose allows water to pass through it from one point in space to another, our bodies allow the vital energy of life to pass through us from one point in time to another, from our birth to our death. Any impedance to the flow of life will cause pressure to build up in our bodies. This pressure will be experienced as pain.

It is ironic that we often attempt to deal with our pain through a mechanism, the tensing of muscular tissue, that may be largely responsible for the pain in the first place. What we succeed in doing through such a tactic is to drive the initial pain from which we are suffering deeper and deeper, further and further away from our awareness. While the pain may not seem to bother us as much anymore, it also becomes much more difficult to deal with in any effective way. Such a tactic, moreover, will keep on producing new and different areas of physical pain. And so the masking process goes on and on.

Our bodies are the living record of how we have dealt with our struggle with gravity and of the pain that so often ensues. Each of us has found our own unique bodily way of handling our discomforts, be they physical, emotional, or intellectual. Were we able, however, to step into another person's body, the first thing we might do upon awakening to the experience of that body would be to cry out in pain. What works for someone else may not work for us.

But why are we not crying out in pain ourselves? Our bodies bear witness to the presence of pain. Yet many of us go around in life as though everything were fine, as though everything were working to our satisfaction, or at least in the direction of it. But what of the pain, and what of the condition of numbness we have accepted in exchange for not having to feel the pain? Would we really rather be numb to life than accept pain as it is and retain the possibility that our life might lead to fruition and flowering? Not to acknowledge the extent of our suffering is to share in one of our common lies with the rest of humanity. As we shall see, the Four Noble Truths contain their own sequential logic, so that in refusing to experience our pain, we cut ourselves off from the possibility for its dissolution. Pretending just does not work.

Pain possesses its own wisdom. In fact, pain may be seen as the avenue to wisdom. This does not at all mean that pain should be morbidly pursued for its own sake. It does mean, however, that the ability to experience pain, simply to accept it as it is without reaction, is a necessary precondition for wisdom and insight. Reaction usually takes the form of suppression (pretending that our pain doesn't exist) or dramatization (becoming affected by our pain as though it were the only thing that exists). Either form of reaction moves us away from the simple acceptance of what's real.

By letting go of the notion that pain is somehow our enemy, we can begin to view it as a source of great intelligence. In this way it can be of enormous value to us. Pain draws our attention to the fact that an area in our body is in need of healing. The acute pain that we feel from a broken bone or deep cut is very difficult to silence, and we rightly interpret this sensation as telling us that we require immediate medical attention. Chronic pain, on the other hand, is usually much easier to ignore, or at least to put up with. We do this by removing it to the background of our awareness. In the form of damage to the nervous system or long-term degenerative disease, it too may require medical care. A great deal of low-level chronic pain, however, is the direct result of imbalance in the structure of the body and may be largely emotional or energetic in origin. This is the pain we are sometimes so successfully able to silence. The tragedy, however, is that the pain is attempting quite brilliantly to make us aware of places in our body where our vital energy has become stagnant or blocked.

When we become aware of the presence of pain, we generally speak of it as an object, as a thing outside of and separate from ourselves. In fact, what most of us want from any therapeutic experience is to emerge from it with our familiar sense of self fundamentally intact, but with the rough edges of our lives smoothed out. However, if we truly take the message of our pain to heart, our current sense of self will undergo irreversible alteration. Pain is a constant reminder of our fragmentation. It's as though we have constructed an image of ourselves by accepting certain of the multiple facets of our being and rejecting others. But that which we have rejected cannot disappear. It cries out, rather, in the form of pain. True health and balance can be regained only through reaccepting what we have rejected outright or are passively resisting. The act of healing ourselves is one of reclaiming the energy and vitality that we turned our back on at some point.

The parable of the prodigal son beautifully illustrates this process of fragmentation, the suffering that arises from it, and the possibility of our becoming whole again. The prodigal son represents our fragmented sense of self; the father is our source of life and vital energy. The son turns his back on his father's way of life and goes out into the world on his own. But such an action is destined to failure, and he meets with much suffering. In despair, he returns home to ask his father's forgiveness. This act of coming home, of accepting again as part of ourselves that which we formerly rejected, is cause for great rejoicing. Once again we embrace the very source from which we spring.

The Second Noble Truth, then, is an explicit extension of the first. Suffering is a function of rejection and nonacceptance, of desiring a condition that does not currently exist and not acknowledging the condition that does. And the Third Noble Truth is implicit in the second. A state of true contentment is a function of accepting the truth of what is, rather than desiring or craving that which is not.

An imbalanced body experiences pain. Struggling with our pain in an attempt to change it or get rid of it will only serve to encourage its persistence. By accepting it for what it is, by owning up to it, we initiate a process that has the power to dissolve our pain and to transform its numbing presence into a wave of vital energetic flow.

To arrive at this feeling of vitality and flowering, we must allow ourselves to experience our body. We must accept that experience without manipulating or interpreting what we find in any way. One of the first things that we are likely to meet will be sensations of pain. These sensations may be dull and cover broad areas of the body, or they may be quite sharp and localized. As we continue to pay attention in this way, we may see that these sensations are not uniform in their appearance, but are subtly textured and shaded.

All we can do, and all we need to do, is just sit and feel the pain. In time it will begin to change. The sensations that form our pain will be replaced by slightly different ones, and then all we need to do is accept the feeling that these new sensations have created. If we can yield to the pain, accepting it exactly as it is, allowing it to move us in whatever direction it sees fit, it will ultimately dissolve itself. If we try to manipulate or control it in any way, we will only prolong it.

If you have continually denied your pain, it is difficult to imagine that the pain itself might be the doorway to its resolution. Yet every time you are able to yield to this process it happens. It may not always be easy or even direct. The discomfort may become much greater before it finally subsides. Before long, however, you will discover that the pain you fear is not a solid, unyielding mass, but is constantly, even if subtly, changing. Wherever there is change, no matter how small it may appear, there is the prospect for transformation. Pain is not a force that can maintain equilibrium or homeostasis; it demands resolution. An important key to the success of this process lies in the ability to develop a deep trust in the wisdom of the body. As you immerse yourself in this wholesome trust, it becomes much easier to move forward with hope.

Our goal is to uncover again our natural embodied state, to recover the energy of our body and of life itself. Through such acceptance the process of flowering may begin. It is not a process that can be forced into happening. Life, if yielded to, will initiate this process of its own accord. Eventually, we may be able to train ourselves not to limit the sphere of our acceptance. In the beginning, however, we must turn our attention to what is closest to home, and for many of us this will be the pain we feel. To be alive may be inherently painful, and yet to acknowledge this truth need not be cause for tears. On the contrary, to become reconciled with our pain is a blessed act, for not only does our pain constantly urge us to begin the process of reunification, it also shows us the way.

Body

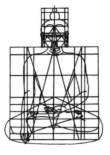

"The word is not the thing."
Alfred Korzybski

*T*o begin this process of reunification we need to be able to feel the body. This may sound simple enough, but the fact is that, for most of us, our body is primarily a concept and only secondarily an experience. As an experiment you can ask someone to describe to you a certain part of their body — let's say their left hand. In most cases what you will get is a description of what their hand looks like, an image of the hand seen from outside itself. The person will describe things such as general shape and color of the hand, the network of lines and ridges that covers the surface of the skin, the appearance of the hair on the top of the hand and fingers, and the difference between the texture of the nails and the skin. The description may even mention the various functions that the hand can perform through the intricate and coordinated movements of the fingers. While all of this is "true" and accurate, it also has nothing at all to do with the experience of the hand.

For a moment place your left hand behind your back where you can no longer see it, and allow yourself to experience what your left hand feels like from inside itself. From this perspective your description will be entirely different. There will be no mention at all of color or distinct shape. The experience that your hand has of itself, if it can be put into words at all, is more of a lightly vibrating feeling of varying pulsation that occupies a space of uncertain shape. The differentiation between where your hand begins and ends is not nearly so clear as it is when the description of your hand is based on what your hand looks like. Furthermore, you may be surprised to discover that the feeling of your hand has a spaciousness to it, as though it seems to occupy a much larger space than your eye tells you it does.

Using words to describe your hand, even the feeling of it, you remove yourself from the simple and direct experience. Allowing your hand to experience and know itself, you enter into a world of pure sensation in which words have no place.

One of the philosophical approaches that Ida Rolf particularly enjoyed as support for her vision of the body was Korzybski's theory of General Semantics. In it he deals with the effect that words have on human beings. Korbyzski calls attention to the fact that human beings live on silent, objective, physiological levels. Words are created through the interposition of a brain and have nothing to do with how the body is feeling. The world of words gradually removes us from that feeling as our immediate experience becomes progressively abstracted. The initial movement toward abstraction begins by naming our feelings: pleasure, pain, love, anger, etc. In the second order of abstraction we begin juggling the matter of the first order by making statements about these names. The third order works off the second order, and so on. Very soon we are relating through broad philosophical concepts that have little to do with the original impulse from which they distantly arose. Reality is the experience that the body has at the silent level. Everything else is an order of abstraction.

One of our major achievements as a species is our ability to function abstractly. Very few, if any, other animal species are able to relate amongst themselves through even the most rudimentary abstractions. As long as it is accepted and acknowledged for what it is, abstract thought serves us in magnificent ways. However, if it is not so acknowledged, we stand the danger of losing touch with the true ground of human existence, the tactile reality of our bodies. When this occurs, we are in trouble.

An understanding of this distinction is central to the process of reunification that we are talking about. Our tendency is to withdraw into the world of conceptual abstraction to keep from feeling the reality of our body's life. We remove ourselves from the raw and vital experience of the body and instead become a "something" (a concept) that "has" (a concept) a "body" (a concept). Increasingly we come to know ourselves through our concepts and identify ourselves with the words we have created to describe our attributes: man, woman, old, young, happy, miserable, good-looking, ugly, rich, poor, and on and on. That we exist in the form of a physical body becomes just another item in our conceptual catalog of descriptive attributes.

However, the experience of our left hand and of every other part of the body knows nothing of any of this. It knows only of a silent, wordless feeling, a tactile presence that pulsates and shimmers in a world of its own. The varieties of tactile sensation contained within the body are virtually limitless. Some of the sensations may be quite pleasurable, appearing as subtly tingling electrical currents flowing through broad areas of the body. Others may be extremely painful and unpleasant, appearing as intensified, aching throbs. Like electrical lights being rapidly turned on and off, all the sensations, even the most persistently uncomfortable, pulsate at varying rates and speeds. Pleasurable sensations tend to vibrate at very high rates of frequency, unpleasant sensations at significantly slower rates.

It is one thing to be able to experience individual sensations by focusing on specific parts of the body. It is yet another to be able to feel the entire body in a single moment of perception. The ability to experience the whole body as a unified field of tactile sensation initiates a remarkable shift in awareness that challenges the most basic assumptions we hold about ourselves in particular, and the nature of reality in general. The reason for this is that experiencing the whole body at a sensational level forces us out of the world of concepts and into the world of experience. It's as though we suddenly draw open a shade that has long obscured a window and vista we never even knew existed. An alternative vision of the world, radically different from the one we have become familiar with, is suddenly exposed.

As we exist right now, most of us have only limited access to the world of experience. What we call pain is one of the only feelings with which we are regularly in contact, and this feeling we often attempt to suppress. We know that the body is of one piece, but there is nothing at all unified about the highly random and disjointed awareness we have of it. When we broaden our focus to include a greater awareness of bodily experience, we are often confronted with a lopsided and imbalanced mass of sensations. One side of the body may predominate over the other. We may feel the front of the body more than the back, the top half more than the bottom, or any combination of these. Only very rarely do we feel unified. We exist, rather, much like Humpty-Dumpty after the fall, and like him the task before us is to put our body back together again into a single piece.

As we turn our attention inward, back to the feeling of our body, many interesting things begin to happen. You may recall that when you were focusing on your left hand there came a moment when the concept of your hand vanished completely, and all that was left was the tactile experience of your hand. At this moment your hand "knew" itself. Ordinarily we think of the generation of knowledge as being inseparable from the brain's ability to combine basic linguistic building blocks into a meaningful pattern of conceptual imagery. However, the knowledge we are referring to here is tactile knowledge. It is essentially nonverbal and, consequently, has nothing whatsoever to do with this aspect of the brain. It exists as a basic cellular property, one that can only be apprehended through our sense of tactility. Like our more conventional knowledge, it too requires a good deal of training before we can become conversant with the information it is capable of revealing. In time, and with much patient practice, the experience that you have become aware of in your left hand can expand to include the whole body. In the face of such an awareness, your conventional sense of self will begin to dissolve. There will be no "you" to know your body; rather, your body will know itself.

Our senses are the connecting link between the inner and outer worlds. The information we receive through them, however, is vastly different, depending on whether the awareness of the body is oriented more toward concept or experience. Locking ourselves into a primarily conceptual framework interferes with our body's ability to function in its most vital way. A tendency toward conceptualization creates a rift between ourselves and the world. Our eyes may be open, but we don't necessarily see what is in front of us. Such vision is at best highly selective, and the same is true for our other senses as well. Often we eat without tasting our food or pass through a garden of flowers without the slightest awareness of its fragrance.

Sounds and tactile sensations are always present; yet we somehow filter out a great deal of the available incoming data. At moments like these, we are not fully present to interact with life. Where we are is adrift inside the endless monologue of fantasies, thoughts, opinions, and observations that dominate the inner landscape of our conceptual mind. This world exists within the narrow confines of our skulls.

To become grounded in the experience of our body is to embrace the world once again. To accept the body is to accept what is conveyed through our senses. When we drop our tendency to conceptualize, not only do our eyes, when open, see precisely what is in front of them, but the world outside comes suddenly flooding into us through the passageway of vision. Our experience at this moment is that the world outside is not "outside," separate from and unrelated to our body, but exists rather as an inseparable aspect of our experience of embodiment. We become the co-creators of this world, the context within which the physical universe, as we perceive it from moment to moment, exists. In a later chapter we will expand on this idea in detail.

This distinction between conceptual and experiential awareness is paralleled in the Buddhist distinction between neurosis and health. A neurotic mind is viewed as being strongly conditioned by the notion of an exclusive separation between our inner and outer worlds. From this perspective, the body is conceived as a shell or container. What is inside the body is somehow exclusively me; what is outside the body is partly the domain of others and partly a kind of no-man's-land. In Buddhist psychology this is simply an erroneous notion that has no basis in experience. Holding on to such a notion blocks the exchange of vital energy between body and environment, and such blockage gives rise to the never ceasing flow of mental chatter which, among other things, would have us believe that this notion is, in fact, an accurate reflection of reality. Without an accurate understanding of what is real, we have no choice but to become lost and confused.

A healthy mind, on the other hand, is a function of what in Buddhist psychology is termed *sunyata* or "open dimension of being." We become open to the actual experience of life, accepting it as it is without any attempt to modify or cosmeticize it, without any urgency to add words of explanation to what we are so directly experiencing. Within such an experience of openness, separation and distinction have no ground, and our ordinarily unrelenting sense of isolation begins to break down. The dissolution of this artificially created barrier will be accompanied almost immediately by an easing of pain and by an increase in our awareness of pulsation and vibratory flow. The opacity of our pain becomes increasingly transparent as we come to realize that even within the experience of pain there is fundamentally nothing of immutable substance to be found.

As we learn to shift from conceptualization into experience, we acquire a fundamental skill that is of primary importance as we continue on our journey toward balance and flowering. To familiarize yourself with the world of bodily sensation, you may find it helpful to move your attention systematically through your body from one part to the next. Simply allow that part of your body to know itself at that moment. You may feel nothing, you may feel pain, you may feel pulsation or tingling, or you may feel a sensation that you have no adequate words to describe. The labels that you use to describe the different qualities of sensation are of little importance. What is important is that you are able to perceive the sensation exactly as it is. Bodies, much like the world of which they are a part, are continually in states of flux and change. One day a certain sensation may exist for you in a certain part of your body; the next day the sensation you find in that part of the body may be entirely different. As much as you can, stay focused solely on sensation during this exercise. If, while doing this, any mental image of that bodily part gets added to the awareness of sensation, simply acknowledge the presence of this conceptualization and patiently bring your attention back again to the level of sensation. In this way you can quickly begin to appreciate that what we refer to as "body" is quite different depending on whether our orientation comes primarily through concept or experience.

It is important to remind ourselves time and again that our journey proceeds by accepting what is real. This does not mean forcing an awareness of bodily sensation or condemning and suppressing our urge to conceptualize. Both are real for us, both will be there, and so both must be accepted. As we begin focusing on specific places of pain, a great deal of conceptual association may emerge along with the penetrating awareness of sensation. What we need to cultivate is the ability to distinguish clearly between what is concept and what is bodily experience. In this way we learn to see things clearly. We become more conversant with the exact nature of the components of reality. The ability to perceive the body for what it is makes the prospect of losing our way on the journey of awakening significantly less likely.

Time, Present Time, and Change

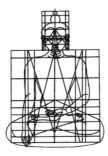

*B*y paying attention to the sensations of the body, we gain insight into the mystery of time. Our normal understanding of time is based on our acceptance of the concepts of past, present, and future. The past is all that is behind us, the future is everything yet to come, and the present is the point between these. Seen in this way, our concept of time is closely related to our concept of space. As we move along a path, there is space in front of and behind us, and our body seems to occupy the space in which we stand at this very moment.

Common to both is a quality of extension that ascribes a sense of reality not only to the present moment of experience, but to the time and space surrounding that moment as well. Tomorrow and yesterday are just as real for us as the present moment. As we move from point to point, we do so with the certainty that both our destination and point of departure — even through we cannot experience them in the present moment — are just as real as the ground on which we walk.

Taken together, our concept of time and space creates the image of the world in which we live. Together they form the stage on which the drama of life is played. Together they enable our lives to unfold in a coherent and continuous manner. Seen in this way, the passage of time is not so much a function of the universe as it is an *a priori* condition that allows the play of the universe to appear.

Within this concept of time, it is very easy to identify what is past and future, but quite a bit more difficult to pinpoint the present moment with any precision or certainty. Our past is a continually expanding entity, our future a continuously shrinking one. The present is that highly elusive dividing line between the two, so unstable as to appear almost illusory. If we attempt to isolate a specific moment, saying "*this* is the present," it has already faded away into the past. It is a little like passing your hand back and forth in front of a television screen. What you see, seemingly at once, is your hand and a whole series of afterimages. Often it is difficult to separate what is real from its afterimage.

Quite a different way of understanding time, however, comes to us when we attend to the experience of the body. Our body can only know itself in this very moment. For our body the ideas of past and future are meaningless. Only the present moment is real. Only the present moment exists. As is often pointed out by Buddhist teachers, past and future exist only as thoughts in the present moment. The past is a function of the mental faculty of memory. The future is a function of the mental faculty of imagination.

Past and future, then, "exist" only in so far as our mode of functioning is predominantly conceptual. As we shift our focus more and more into the experience of our body, past and future simply disappear, and all we are left with is the awareness of a single present moment whose one abiding nature is that it is constantly changing. If we remain lodged in the world of concepts, past and future seem to have a tangibility to them while the present moment is at best a highly elusive flicker. If we are able to move more into the world of our bodily experience, just the opposite is true. Past and future become hollow words. All that exists are the sensations, perceptions, and feelings that are passing through our awareness in this very moment.

It is important to understand that we are not talking about a succession of individual and unique present moments, one following upon another like seconds on a clock. This leads us all too easily back into the idea of past and future time. Only this one present moment exists, but it can never be pinpointed or labeled as such because its contents are perpetually in flux. The present moment arises out of the present moment and disappears into the present moment. Seen another way, this very moment you are born, and in the same moment you pass the entire course of your life and experience your death.

Closely related to such an approach to time are two principles central to Buddhist philosophy: *anicca* and *anatta*. Each can be seen as a function of the other, as two sides of the same coin. *Anicca* is the recognition of the impermanent, continually changing nature of life. Everything comes and goes; nothing remains or lasts. Experiences, sensations, thoughts, and feelings — none of it is permanent. Things arise seemingly out of nowhere, enter into our field of awareness where they linger for a moment, and then disappear. Closely aligned with this principle is the notion of *anatta* — the recognition that nothing like a permanent self exists in us, and that we too, at both the surface and depth of experience, are part of the great onrushing river of life, ever changing, and ever shifting.

We have been conditioned from early childhood to believe in the existence of a self, an "I." But as we move more fully into the experience of our body, we begin to get glimpses that the idea of a permanent self is nothing more than an idea, just another concept although admittedly a very deep-rooted one. Just as the principles of *anicca* and *anatta* arise together or not at all, so does the belief in the existence of a "self" arise as a function of our conceptual model of time. We tend to know ourselves more through our past and future than we do through the experience of the present moment. Our past gives us our identity. Our future offers promise of the forging of that identity. Attaching a sense of self to our remembered experiences and unformed possibilities, we quickly become a something moving through time.

One of the clearest, most direct ways in which to realize the truths of *anicca* and *anatta* is to attend to the tactile sensations of our body. If we attempt to locate anything substantive or stable within the experience of the body, we come up empty-handed. If we move our awareness into any part of our body, what we encounter is an experience of vibration and pulsation, a shimmer and glow ever changing in its sensation. Sometimes the pulsation is intense and obvious; at other times it becomes very subtle — a soft, almost imperceptible tingle. Sometimes the body experiences itself as a solid, compacted mass; at other times it expands and dissolves into an airy and open-ended feeling of spaciousness. It can feel warm one moment and chilled the next. Because our minds have the notion that our bodies exist as solid objects, we tend to see them so. But as our awareness becomes more precise and we begin to experience the body as a pulsating and flowing mass of sensations, the world that we live in begins to pulsate and flow as well. What we previously observed to be hard-edged becomes gradually less distinct. Objects slowly lose their sense of fixed solidity and instead become more like an undulating wave of heat seen across a desert plain or a waterfall in continual motion.

In the southern part of Asia where Buddhism is practiced, a person who has come to realize that everything is in constant flux is referred to as a "stream-winner." It is a beautiful and appropriate term. For such a person the world must seem similar to a flowing brook. No longer does a stream-winner view him or herself as a separate, static entity moving through time and space. What exists instead is an awareness of oneself as a process of flow and change--one moment one thing, the next moment another. A stream-winner becomes whatever is moving across his or her field of awareness at that particular moment, and yet identifies with none of it.

The only thing that can remain constant through all this is the experience of the present moment. To be present is to be aware. At one moment, one sensation is dominant, and our awareness comprehends this clearly. The next moment a new sensation appears, and our awareness moves to it. Our sense of isolation — of a self separate and distinct from the rest of life — results from clinging to certain of the images and sensations that move through us, from trying to capture and hold on to one of the ever changing sensations in the flow of life, and from attempting to stop the process of *anicca* and freeze it. But such action is as futile as trying to hold back and contain the power of the ocean with a dam made of sand; it is also very painful. To reinforce a sense of "I" is to fight with the energy of life and give up the incredible ease of a naturally flowing stream.

It is easy for us to sit mesmerized by the beauty of a waterfall. More than with most things in life, it is a very obvious manifestation of the truth of constant change. Imagine for a moment that somehow that waterfall could know itself, that somehow it could have a conscious experience of itself. Millions of distinct droplets of water pass through it every minute. The sun creates constantly changing patterns of iridescence in its mist. As the water strikes the rocks and pool below, an unending murmur of sound is produced. With its form being created and disappearing every instant, the waterfall could only know itself from moment to moment in its ever changing pattern. To think that the waterfall would choose to identify with any one aspect of its experience--say a specific droplet of water as it comes cascading down, or a particular band of color in the rainbow that adorns it--is absurd, and yet this is exactly what we do.

As we grow older, we encounter an enormous variety of experiences. Some of these pass through us easily, but others leave a more lasting, indelible impression. We identify with them more. It is these experiences that strongly contribute and add to our growing sense of self, our growing sense of "I-ness." It is almost as though the event or thought leaves an imprint or stain on our faculty of awareness. Gradually we begin experiencing ourselves and the world through the bias of this imprint. In so doing, we begin to lose touch with the unobstructed stream-like movement of life and enter instead into a more stagnant and frozen condition. We also lose touch with the clarity that comes from being grounded in the present moment and enter into a much more complicated world of time.

Only when we let go of our suppositions and give up all notions of any personal substantiality do we realize the one eternal focus of our existence, the experience of the present moment. It is not, however, by withdrawing from the passing sensations of life, but rather by experiencing them to the fullest that we are best able to uncover that silent and mysterious sense of being that seems to lie always just underneath their surface. The stream knows that none of its sensations are eternal. They come and go like actors on a stage. And yet it invests itself as fully as it possibly can in the drama of which it's a part. The trick for us is to learn how to immerse ourselves in life while remaining untainted or unstained by any of it, just as the oil on a duck's feathers allows it to remain dry even as it immerses itself in a pond. The next few chapters will offer suggestions as to how that might be accomplished.

Surrender

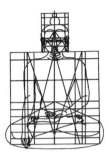

*T*o accept whatsoever life brings us is to embrace, and in turn be embraced by, the intelligence of life. Most animals and the entire realm of plant life cannot do otherwise. A plant, for example, could not be more perfectly surrendered to the life force that animates it. It has, in the conventional sense, no "mind" of its own. In the course of its life it sprouts from a fertilized seed, grows to maturity, flowers, and then decays. Man's life follows a similar course with the exception that only a small percentage of men and women really flower. If we surrender ourselves to the flow of life, flowering follows as a natural consequence. If we fight with life, however, we may miss this event entirely, and so we die with bitterness and regret.

The Buddha observed that suffering results from our inability to surrender to life, to accept the conditions of our life just as they are and just as they come to us. Whenever we want the situation in which we find ourselves to be different from what it is, we create suffering for ourselves. Whenever we accept our present situation exactly as it is, without manipulating or tempering it in any way, we free ourselves from our suffering. Resistance creates a claustrophobic quality to our experience; we feel hemmed in and compressed. Acceptance, on the other hand, generates a feeling of openness and spaciousness. Resistance causes our body to recoil and contract. Involuntarily we tighten, bracing ourselves against the presence of the object we are resisting. Only through acceptance are we able to come to balance. With nothing to resist, our bodies can relax, and out of this relaxation balance is born.

The importance of acceptance is expressed in a story about the Sufi mystic who, in spite of the hardships he and his disciples were facing, continued to pray and affirm his gratitude to God. After a long and tiring journey, they had come to a village in the middle of the night, hoping to find shelter. But the villagers were frightened by this mysterious band of travelers and would not allow them to enter.

They were forced to withdraw instead to an unprotected hill. The night was col and they did not have enough clothing or blankets to keep them warm. From ever direction they could hear the cries of wild animals. There was little food to ea And still the mystic prayed, extending his gratefulness to God for providing hi and his followers everything they required. One of his disciples, on overhearin his prayers, became highly agitated and challenged his master to explain what h meant. On this night the disciple felt his master's expression of gratitude was false show, and he told him so. His master, however, was a simple man whos understanding had come about through a deep trust in the perfection of life. Withou guile he turned to his disciple and replied simply: "Yes, what I said before I repe again. God gives me whatsoever I need. Tonight I need poverty. Tonight I nee feeling rejected. Tonight I need to be hungry, in danger. Otherwise, why wou he give it to me?"

To respond to life in such an open and accepting way is difficult for us. Th reason for this is that, like the disciple in the story, we have been strongly conditione by our attachment to pleasurable sensations and our reaction to unpleasant one If something pleasant arises, we attempt to cling to it, to hold it to ourselves. something unpleasant arises, we try to push it away. Both actions are attempts t manipulate the natural course of life, both require a great deal of effort to perforn and through either one we forfeit the grace that only surrender can provide.

But how can we bring about this process of surrender within ourselves? Ho can we reeducate ourselves and learn once again what it means to accept uncor ditionally what life places in our path? By its very nature, surrender is not an activit that can be rehearsed and later performed; it is much more spontaneous than tha Surrender does not come through effort and force, but rather through yielding. is a process of allowance, an acknowledgement of the most fundamental forces th shape our lives. On a practical, physical level, this can most easily be experience by acknowledging the effect gravity has on our body. To give in to gravity, to allo the weight of our body to drop in response to the pull of gravity, is to enter int a condition of surrender.

Most of us, however, live as bodies that are in conflict with gravity. We rema erect only through struggle and effort. If we were truly to surrender and let g to relax those muscles whose habitual tensing provides us with our source of suppor we would feel the various segments of our body giving way until we fell to th earth. Our task, then, is to alter our relationship with the gravitational field in suc a way that allows us to remain standing as effortlessly as if we were lying dow on the ground or floating in a pool of salt water. To reacquire the ability to stan without effort is to regain the support of the universe.

The key to such a transformation is two-fold. The first requirement is a bod whose structure is compactly and symmetrically aligned around an imaginar vertical axis. It is primarily through a more vertical stacking of the major segment of the body that our relationship with gravity can begin to shift. A body that ha strayed from optimal alignment experiences gravity as a negative force again which it must brace itself to stand up. To counteract the deteriorating effect of gravity it must provide its own source of support to remain erect. On the other hand, a body whose segments are situated in a predominantly vertical relationship to one another generates its support through the very fact of its verticality. Its uprightness is reinforced by gravity, and its experience of gravity is primarily as a source of buoyancy.

As our body becomes increasingly aligned around a vertical axis, we enter into a whole new relationship with gravity in which surrender becomes possible. Now as we stand erect, we can allow our weight to drop, and instead of tumbling to the ground our body will spontaneously make the subtle adjustments necessary to keep us upright. Being able to drop our weight in this way is literally to give up our burden in life. The conditions that keep us from becoming rooted in the soil of life begin to drop away. The ability to surrender the weight of the body to gravity is a prerequisite for healing. Verticality allows for bodily surrender. Surrender, in turn, leads to flowering.

To surrender to gravity is to surrender deeply into the experience of the body. It cannot be otherwise. The holding that is necessary to keep an imbalanced body upright also serves to deaden the experience of that body. As this pattern of holding begins to drop away, an often chaotic flood of strong physical sensations, emotions, and associated mental images may emerge and sweep over us. If we can allow these feelings and sensations to travel through us however they wish, we can release the confining pattern of holding. If these feelings become too intense for us to bear, we can stop them--and return to a more familiar, although less dynamic, experience of being--by once again tensing those parts of our body whose chronic contraction creates that more familiar experience. The impulse to tense in the face of the emerging sensations is a virtually automatic one so when you begin to experiment with this kind of release you will find that the difficulty will not lie in your inability to reduce the strong rush of bodily sensation, but in allowing it to continue without reverting back to your conventional pattern of holding.

Anyone who has experimented with any of the forms of somatic therapy is familiar with this process. The experience of being Rolfed, for example, can be quite intense, especially when the Rolfer is working on an area of chronic contraction and holding. If we are able to accept the intensity of the sensation and respond to it naturally, we are often led, both physically and emotionally, to the experience of its release. If, however, the sensation reaches a level of intensity that we feel incapable of accepting, we often react by tightening the part of the body that is being touched (or a compensating part) in an attempt to push the sensation--and the Rolfer's hands--away. At some point, however, we come to realize that such resistance both increases the intensity of the sensation and interferes with the possibility for its release.

Whenever something, even the most pleasurable kind of sensation, becomes "too much," it becomes a source of pain for us. The point beyond which an acceptable sensation becomes too much to bear is a crucial one because it is exactly at this point that we lose our ability to surrender and begin, instead, to react. It is this reaction, this attempt to modify or subdue a sensation's intensity, that transforms that sensation into a pain. Every moment of reaction, be it pushing away or clinging, is dependent on muscular effort and tensing, and each unnecessary moment of muscular tensing locks us further into a condition of conflict with gravity.

Our ability to respond to situations of strong intensity is closely related to our ability to surrender the weight of the body to gravity and stand in relatively effortless balance. They are different manifestations of the same process; one either feeds the other or inhibits the other's possibility. A body that is in harmony with the gravitational field can allow even the strongest and most intense sensations to manifest through it without interfering with them. In this way, no trace of the event is left behind in the tissues of the body. It gets consumed completely. A body that is in conflict with gravity is imbalanced, at least partially anyway, because sensations become "too much" for it to experience through to their completion. A body that holds itself rigidly to stand up must also hold itself rigidly in the face of a strong feeling. Such a body carries around with it a whole host of unfinished or incomplete situations recorded within its cells. What appears to happen is that the memory of the situation becomes frozen in the flesh that has tightened in reaction to it.[2] As the residue from this pattern of reaction accumulates, surrender and balance become even more elusive.

In Buddhist psychology this residue forms the basis for what are called the *sankharas*, the reactive mental formations that cloud our inner space and keep us locked in a cycle of confusion. Reactions take literal form in the flesh of the body, and over a period of time we become imprisoned within a contracted web of tissue. As we consciously begin to surrender the weight of our body to gravity, we allow for layer upon layer of these accumulated *sankharas* to come to the surface of awareness and be released. The release will often manifest at both physical and mental levels, as the fascial holding that sustains the reactive mental formations softens to allow for their release. Nothing need be done with the sensations, feelings, and images as they emerge. They are not data for us to ponder over, figure out, or analyze. Just to experience them is enough. They emerge into our field of awareness at their own speed, and they release at their own speed. All we can profitably do is observe this process of appearance and change without interfering with it and let nature take its course.

---

2) A theory that many somatic therapists find particularly attractive is that the repository for the portion of our minds that remains largely unconscious is not some remote corner of the brain, but is rather the soft tissue of the body itself. Our current models of mind and consciousness are not adequate to explain just how this psychic material becomes lodged in bodily tissue. Nonetheless, evidence that the process of Rolfing has revealed increasingly suggests that this observation is an accurate one. On many an occasion the release of a highly contracted, and consequently quite tender, area of soft tissue is accompanied by the release of the memory of an earlier incident (often a quite distressing one) which had, until that moment, been "forgotten." Whether the memory is actually stored somehow in the tissue proper, or whether the fascial release stimulates the extrication of the memory from some mechanism within the nervous system is not clear. What is clear, however, is that the soft tissue plays a central role in the storage of the memory.

Allowing this process to unfold over time will affect and alter our sense of self, sometimes quite dramatically. Much of what we had previously considered to be intrinsic qualities of ourselves may suddenly appear far less important, and the constant chatter of our mind will begin slowly to diminish and dissolve. It is this constant chatter that continually reaffirms the often erroneous views and notions that we hold so dearly about ourselves and the world. If in our surrender we can arrive at a place of complete effortless balance, our mind may stop completely, even if only for a moment. Then, for the first time perhaps, the enormously open and spacious nature of our being can reveal itself.

As we become more sensitive and aware through our surrender, we come to realize that what in Buddhist psychology is termed ego--our sense that we exist somehow as an entity separate and distinct from the rest of life--is simply a function of bodily holding, of the particular pattern of chronic muscular tensing through which our bodies most familiarly resist gravity. The stuff of which our bodies are made is intrinsically pliant and malleable. Yet out of the wide range of physical possibilities available to us, we have chosen a single, predominant mold with which we inhibit ourselves. Over time the gelatinous tissues of the body become set in the mold and harden. The quality of consciousness that manifests through a body that is set in such a way exhibits all the attitudes that we normally associate with egoic mind.[3] Soften the frozen structural pattern, and the static and alienated quality of mind begins to soften as well.

When spiritual teachers speak of dropping the mind or dropping the ego, they mean just that: to drop it, to allow it (or, more precisely, the holding that is sustaining it) to fall to the earth. Through the action of dropping, it dissolves. What is actually dropping away is the persona, the mask that we have created as a buffer to protect ourselves not only from the real or imagined threats of the world outside our body, but also from the intensified sensations and mental imagery of our inner world as well. All of us have the same name for this aspect of ourselves: we call it "I." Through it we project a limited image of ourselves that we mistakenly equate as our true identity. One of the primary goals of our persona is to trick other people into making the same mistake when they relate to us. Hidden behind this fictive buffer, we believe we have some control over the way we are seen. Only by manipulating the tactile experience of the body through a precise pattern of muscular holding are we able to create and sustain a persona. Such a strategy, however, is based on denying the body as it truly is. Ultimately it can only lead to disappointment and confusion. Like a house of cards that believes itself far more substantial than it is, our persona condemns us to a life of suffering if we choose to identify with the image it deludes us into believing is real.

---

3) The more common word "egotistic" distorts the intended meaning, and so the word "egoic" will be used throughout this book. "Egotistic" refers to someone who has an overly lofty vision of one-self and is generally insufferable to be around. "Egoic" refers to the held belief that who I am is an entity named "I," the speaker of the monologue inside my head. Virtually everybody in the West has been conditioned to experience themselves as "egoic." Hopefully, not everyone is "egotistic."

Only when this mask begins to drop away can we begin to appreciate its superficial nature. In terms of the experience of our body, the persona can be felt to exist exactly where a mask would fit, just at the surface of the body. By identifying with the persona, we block out all access to deeper, more spacious areas of our bodily life, sometimes so effectively that we may never realize that these areas exist at all. Hidden just beneath our persona is the dynamic world of the body: unfiltered, raw, and very vital. Within this world there is nothing of enduring substance that lasts longer than the briefest flicker. Everything is in the process of appearance and dissolution. By familiarizing ourselves with this process, we clarify the nature of identity. By accepting ourselves as we are, we realize what is truly unique about ourselves.

If we hold back and refuse to enter into this experience of dissolution, our sense of self as a separate entity remains intact, but our vital energy suffers. Chronic pain becomes common. If we are courageous enough to surrender the weight of our body to the field of gravity, our various masks fall away, and the phenomenon of dissolution begins to occur. Our mind and body begin to shimmer, and painful blockages in the body, like intractable, frozen particles suddenly exposed to a source of heat, spontaneously begin to resolve themselves. True vitality and the fascial integrity that sustains it are only available to a body that has learned to give up its attachment to a sense of separateness. The irony, of course, is that while we fear the prospect of this dissolution, it offers us the prospect of lasting fulfillment. These, then, are our choices, and to a large extent it is a matter of choice.

Surrendering to gravity in this way gradually recreates a feeling of unity. The experience of body becomes more integrated and uniform throughout. Recovering this sense of bodily unification provides us with the foundation necessary for the ongoing process of flowering. In the literature of Buddhism this process is referred to as "enlightenment." Enlightenment, from all accounts, is not about becoming something other than what we already are. It is about reclaiming that which is intrinsically ours and always has been. It is a return to our natural state. In this way it can be seen simply as an organic process that should mark one of the natural stages of the growth of the human body, just as does the onset of puberty. But unlike puberty or birth or death, enlightenment must be actively chosen. It must be allowed. For some strange reason we have the ability to block it from happening to us. Our bodies are designed to experience the fulfillment of flowering. Our bodies *want* to be enlightened, and yet we cling to the familiar and most often choose the security of the seed. Through the action of surrender we can begin to reverse this familiar pattern and open up the way for the gradual cessation of our suffering.

The Middle Way

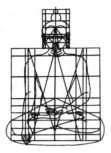

*T*he term "to stand without effort" requires some clarification so as not to be misleading. A certain amount of muscular effort is necessary for any action the body can perform. This is true not only for something as obvious as moving a large object, but for something as subtle as standing without effort as well. A small amount of contraction is still evident in the fibers of a healthy muscle when it comes to rest. This natural condition of slight contraction is what is called muscle tone. Proper muscle tone is always in evidence in a healthy body, even one that has surrendered its weight completely to gravity and is "standing without effort." True surrender, then, creates appropriate muscle tone, not flaccidity. For any action the appropriate amount of effort is "effortless."

A body that habitually uses more muscular effort than is necessary for what it is doing is said to be hypertonic--possessing too much tone. Such a body, even at rest, is often tense and compressed, as though it contains too much energy. A body that habitually uses less muscular effort than is appropriate for a given task is said to be hypotonic--possessing too little tone. Such a body will often experience itself as listless or dull, as lacking in energy. At both extremes the body fatigues easily, although the hypertonic body may be less willing to admit and accept its fatigue. Within the metaphor of the previous chapter, verticality without surrender (the traditional military posture) creates a hypertonic condition. A body that has experienced a certain amount of letting go but does not have a structure adequate to support its surrender (one accustomed to depressant drugs) becomes hypotonic.

The goal, of course, is to find and abide in that place just in the middle. Well-toned tissue encourages the most efficient transfer of nutrients and waste between the blood stream and the cells. It also provides the most beneficial medium for nerve impulses to pass through. Such tissue is in harmony with itself; its tone is neither too sharp nor too flat. It feels right.

The Buddha called his path "The Middle Way." His life prior to his enlightenment had been one of extremes. He was born a prince and grew up with all the finest material comforts. Later, when he left his home and family to search for a more meaningful way to live his life, he went to the opposite extreme and undertook a variety of severe ascetic practices that were common amongst spiritual seekers of that era. Ultimately, he found that neither extreme worked, but that somewhere just in the middle was the key he had been looking for. Neither too far to the left, nor too far to the right, but just in the middle, in a condition of balance, did he find what he was seeking.

Weight, Weightlessness, and Grace

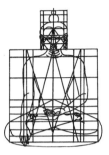

A body in conflict with gravity experiences unnecessary heaviness and weight. It holds itself up through the same kind of muscular tensing that is required to lift a large, cumbersome object. A body in harmony with the gravitational field exists quite differently. The fact of its verticality and balance provide it with all the support it needs. Consequently, there is nothing to hold up. The experience of this body will be predominantly one of lightness and buoyancy.

While a body's weight can be measured on a scale with relative accuracy, that measurement says nothing about how that body experiences its weight. A hundred pound person can feel weighed down and heavy. Someone twice that weight can feel as though they were "walking on air." It all depends on how well or how poorly a body is balanced. In some cultures, for example, people are able to balance extremely heavy objects on their head and transport them with ease over distances that would be unthinkable if they were carrying them in any other way. The same is true of how we move our body from place to place. When the body is not aligned in a predominantly vertical and balanced way, we tire quickly and limit our possibilities. The opposite, of course, is also true.

What we are actually doing when we allow our weight to drop is relaxing those muscles whose chronic contraction creates the experience of weight. Once that relaxation has occurred, any sense of heaviness vanishes as well. It simply drops away. True relaxation, then, is a function of the body's ability to surrender its weight to the pull of gravity.

One of the most commonly mentioned benefits of balance is a sense of lift that accompanies a body's shift toward better alignment. As we align the mass of our body around a more central vertical axis and succeed in altering our relationship with gravity, we often become taller.[4] This, in itself, is not difficult to explain.

---

4) When astronauts who have experienced long periods of weightlessness return to earth, they are often slightly taller than they were before their journey into space. Quite obviously they too have undergone a dramatic, if temporary, alteration in their relationship with gravity. The extra length doesn't last that long, however, once they refamiliarize themselves with the earth's gravitational field.

Structural rotations occurring at the joints may be present in abundance in an imbalanced body. For example, a lower leg might be facing in a slightly different direction from the one the upper leg is oriented toward. The overall effect of this is to decrease the available span of the whole leg. Much of the work of balancing a body centers around undoing rotations, and as the most pronounced rotations unwind the body lengthens.

What is more difficult to explain is the sense of lift and lightness that accompanies this reorganization of bodily structure. The earth's gravitational field draws us down, keeping us literally "earthbound." However, if the body does not have to resist gravity to remain standing, it often feels as though it is expanding upward, as though it is being drawn in the exact opposite direction from the normal gravitational pull. How can this be explained?

In the first place it is not completely accurate to imply that this expansion occurs only in an upward direction even though this may be what it largely feels like. For this upward and outward expansion to occur at all, the body must first be able to allow its weight to drop. The initiating phase of this expansion, then, occurs very much in a downward direction. Our surrender to gravity, the "invisible" part of the process, precedes and allows for this feeling of lift. The two-fold nature of this process is depicted in Figure 1 and bears a metaphoric similarity to the process of growth that is typical of all plant life. The heights to which a tree grows is entirely dependent on how deeply its roots sink into the earth. All that is apparent to our eye is an expansion upward and outward with the passing of each new year.

GRAVITATING

RADIATING

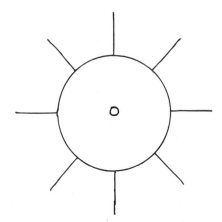

The eye sees more directly than the mouth says.

If I, now named reps, show you *GRAVITATING* as above it can remind you to do it if you see it on a bare wall. As you *EXPERIENCE* gravitating all I-me-mine melts into it and you are free. Every cell and pore of you already gravitates so why resist this silent mighty power in your honor? At least lessen your troubling.

As you let sink down you become weightless and like a seed open UP and RADIATE sunward and nothing can stop you. And nothing can stop you. And nothing can stop you. Each instant new all through.

Figure 1.
Interpretations of drawings originally done by Paul Reps, a twentieth century Western teacher of Zen.

Allowing the weight of our body to drop initiates a powerful energetic reaction in the opposite (upward) direction, just as Newton's law of action and reaction indicates that it should. It is easy to see how this works if the weight we relinquish is external to ourselves. For example, you have probably had the experience of carrying someone "piggyback" on your shoulders. After some distance when you finally let the person down, it may have felt as though your body was floating upward. The same will hold true for relinquishing internal weight. By allowing a burden to drop away (a burden of guilt, a sense of not being okay, a deep-seated emotional scar, or an erroneous belief about oneself or the world), we experience a sensation of lift in its place. Personal breakthroughs of any kind are accompanied by a sense of relief or release. People who undergo a positive experience of this kind speak of being "high." If too long a period of time elapses between these kinds of experiences, we report feeling "low." These descriptions of experience, even if only by a small amount, are descriptions of physical fact as well. Physical release is accompanied by lengthening and expansion throughout the structure of the body.

One of the clearest descriptions of this kind of experience is to be found in religious literature when mystics speak of entering into a state of grace. People who experience this kind of condition speak of feeling "uplifted," as if they are being inexplicably drawn closer to God. The distinction between feeling weightlessly drawn upward and experiencing oneself as heavy and earthbound forms the physiological basis for our traditionally having assigned the heavens as the locus for all that is divine and the depths of the earth as the domain of suffering. People who enter into a condition of grace speak of how momentarily those elements that cause them to suffer have fallen away. Freed of what they perceive to be their darker natures, they become lighter in weight, mood, and appearance. The movements of their body become increasingly "graceful."

While this division between heaven and hell may be metaphorically apt, in reality it does not present an accurate picture. People who strive for the heights of an imagined heavenly condition by resisting the dark pulls of human nature often only succeed in locking themselves further into the condition from which they are seeking release. It is true that we suffer from anger, lust, greed, and hatefulness. We create pain for ourselves whenever we want the circumstances we find ourselves in to be different from what they are, and desire is the common denominator to all these states of mind. However, if these mental states do manifest, and we attempt to deny their presence or even run away from them, we merely fuel their persistence. The ultimate act of irresponsibility is to attribute their appearance in us to be the work of some meddling external adversary, either visible or invisible.

By allowing our weight to drop, we are likely to encounter our private hells. Yet, in doing so, we open up the possibility for our release from the hellish hold that the emerging sensations (while they remain dormant and undetected) have over us. Most of us attempt to avoid what has been called "the dark night of the soul." Every religious and psychological tradition speaks of it--whether in the form of the devil in the desert, the daughters of Mara, a period of painful purification, or one of alienation, loneliness, despair, and mourning. Any enlightened state comes about by passing directly through that "dark night," not in attempting to bypass it discreetly or in pretending that it does not exist. By not allowing our weight to drop, most of us are holding ourselves up and away from an experience of pain. If, however, we can learn to yield to the pain, we make our way to the dawn that so thankfully resolves the darkness of the night. In the final analysis, heaven and hell are not separate places or even forces of experience. Rather, heaven is hell transformed, just as the feeling of weightlessness is the transformation of the tension that keeps us weighed down and heavy into a condition of relaxation and ease.

Breath

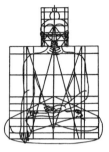

"As you breathe in, o monks, breathe in with the whole body. As you breathe out, o monks, breathe out with the whole body."

Buddha, *Satipatthana Sutta*

"As breath moves through a structurally integrated body, every joint in the body should be able to respond to that movement, and that includes the joints between the small bones in the feet as well as the tiny sutures in the skull."

Ida Rolf

*T*he mass of a balanced structure — be it a building, a tree, or a standing human body—is organized as efficiently as possible around a central, vertical axis. It is the establishment of this axis, or line, that allows the force of gravity to support the structure. The line does not have to be made rigid in order for the structure to maintain its verticality; it has only to be established.

Any attempts to reinforce the weight bearing properties of this central axis by causing it to become less flexible will interfere with its ability to provide support. It is the resilience of the line, not its rigidity, that allows the dynamic process of balance to continue. The tallest trees, and even the tallest buildings, move and sway. They are able to yield to the winds that push against them; if they failed to do this, their resistance would cause them to break apart and fall. The winds that a human body must learn to yield to are primarily internal, produced by the constant inhalation and exhalation of breath.

Breathing, like any physical act, depends upon the coordinated interaction of the musculature of the entire body. So intimately, in fact, are breath and body related that it is misleading to attempt to isolate or observe them separately. They are, rather, different aspects of the same phenomenon. Any tension in the soft tissues of the body interferes with our ability to breathe; any restriction to our pattern of breath causes the body to become stiffer and less fluid in its movement. To hold the body still is to hold the breath still, and vice versa. If the body can free itself of major fascial restrictions, unrestricted breathing follows as an automatic consequence. Its ebb and flow can be clearly observed; its rhythm becomes smooth.

States of mind are influenced and determined not only by bodily structure, but also by patterns of breath. When we are upset or excited, the rhythm of our breath will be noticeably different from when we are feeling loving or calm. When we are comfortable in the presence of someone we care for, our breath is naturally open and full. Exhalations and inhalations follow one upon another with regularity and ease. A sudden surge of anger or agitation immediately disrupts the regularity of this rhythm. The pattern of breath becomes shorter and harsher, increasingly random in the repetition of its phases. If we become disinterested in our life and surroundings, our breath becomes shallow and sunken, its presence scarcely detectible. At death it stops completely.

Resilience, one of the major signs of a balanced body, is intimately connected with the breath. Ordinarily we think of resilience as the ability to move from place to place in a fluid and coordinated manner. True resilience demands the participation of the whole body in concert; one part of the body moves, and every other part responds. Compared with the remarkably resilient bearing of a balanced body, the movement patterns of an imbalanced body will appear stiff and jerky. The body will not move as an integrated whole. Parts of the body will participate in the movement; other parts will be left out completely. Alignment allows a body to come to a static position of balance. Resilience insures that the body will be able to maintain its balance over the course of time.

Resilience begins, however, not with major movements of the body, but with the subtle motion of the breath. The expansion and contraction we associate with breath does not have to be confined to the thorax. It can occur, rather, throughout the whole body. Just as the force that creates ocean swells moves without interference through a body of water, each breath can pass through the entire body in an unimpeded pulsing motion.

A full-bodied pattern of breath depends on relaxation at the joints of the body. If the force of breath encounters a joint that is loose and relaxed, then that joint will be able to yield to the force of breath. Like a billiard ball that has been sent into motion, it will then be able to transfer the force along the span of the adjacent bone on to the next joint of the body. This next joint, in turn, will then be able to yield to the continuation of the force. In this way the simple force of breath can set up a chain reaction of resilient movement throughout the entire length of the body. This pattern is not the norm in adult humans, but then neither are relaxed and balanced bodies. If, however, you observe a sleeping baby or kitten, you will see that this is, in fact, how they breathe.

Full-bodied breathing affords a variety of benefits. It allows a large volume of oxygen to enter into the body upon each inhalation and for an equivalently large volume of gaseous waste to leave the body upon every exhalation. A body that lacks resilience will have a more limited space in which the interchange of oxygen and carbon dioxide can occur. Breath is our life line; it provides us with our single most important nutrient. We can deprive ourselves of the experience of love and caring and live in a diminished condition indefinitely. We can survive without food for several months and without water for several days. But if we go without oxygen for even a few minutes, we die.

Full-bodied breathing keeps our body subtly moving even when sitting or lying down. Bodily movement helps the heart pump blood throughout the circuit of the body, bringing nutrients to each cell and carrying away the accumulated waste. If we eat well, but the nutrients are unable to reach the distant cells of the body, then our food does us little good. A properly functioning lymphatic system insures that each cell of the body can perform its tasks with minimum disruption. The pumping action of the heart has no role at all in moving lymphatic fluid. It is bodily movement that propels the fluid medium of the lymph along its pathways.

Full-bodied breathing is only available if the coordinates of real integration are present within the structure of the body. Once it is available, however, it serves to maintain and even further the balance that allowed for it in the first place. Structural integrity is largely a matter of fascial integrity. The fascia of the body maintains its elasticity, strength, and tone through exercise and movement. When the body remains still, the elastic fibers in the fascia begin to atrophy and lose their ability to recoil and change shape. Full-bodied breathing helps to maintain a body's balance by continually exercising the entire network of fascia in a subtle, but significant, way.

Our breath, then, serves two distinct functions. The first, and most obvious, is to provide the body with oxygen and to remove carbon dioxide. This function is operative in all human beings. Not as critical for our survival, but of significant importance in our quest for well-being, is the breath's less acknowledged ability to keep the body in constant motion — an action that aids in the circulation of bodily fluids and the maintenance of proper fascial tone. This second function operates only in a body that is relaxed and balanced in the gravitational field.[5] Whatever the physiological explanation, there is an undeniable link between the quality of breath and the quality of life. When you are feeling fatigued and constricted, notice how shallow your breath is and how immobile most of your body has become. By engaging in an activity that is strenuous enough to force the breath to deepen, this state of exhaustion will often drop away, cleansing you--for the time being, anyway--of your tension and heaviness.

A naturally occurring full-bodied pattern of breath is quite rare, however. When we begin to observe our breath, watching closely to see how it affects and moves through our body, this is not the pattern we are likely to find. It is much more likely

---

5) An interesting antecedent to this idea can be found in the writings of Emmanuel Swedenborg, an eighteenth century Swedish physician and theoretician. Swedenborg proposed that the primary purpose of the breath was not to provide the body with air, but rather to keep the spinal fluid moving and circulating. This was accomplished through the pumping action that the breath generates in the spine. Each inhalation causes the spine to lengthen and the spinal curves to flatten slightly. Each exhalation causes the spine to contract.

that we will notice some movement in certain areas of the body and very little, if any, movement in others. Just as we can learn to increase our awareness of bodily experience and sensation, so can we also learn to increase the natural fullness of our breath, allowing more and more for our whole body to respond to the flow and movement of respiration. The key, from a somatic perspective, lies in our physical surrender to the gravitational field and in our acceptance of the experience that this surrender generates.

The same muscular tension that creates in us the sensation of heaviness also inhibits our breath. As we allow the weight of our body to drop, our breathing pattern will begin to change automatically. Yielding to the pattern of breath that results from our surrender to gravity, accepting its flow without trying to coerce it into being different in any way, opens the possibility that it may change on its own.[6]

In order for this change to take place, however, we need to bring more and more awareness to the actual process of breathing. This is the Buddhist strategy. The passage of air in and out of the body occurs every moment of our lives, and yet we are rarely aware of its continual movement. If we can shift our customary focus to include a moment to moment awareness of its passage, we can effectively transform this automatic process into a vehicle capable of having a profound influence on our mind and body. By bringing awareness to the breath in this way, we must be careful not to manipulate the respiratory flow in any way. As we patiently observe its natural movement in and out of our body, we will see that it develops a self-propelling momentum. If we can recognize, and then yield to, that momentum, the breath will begin shifting on its own when, and if, it needs to. It will establish a pattern and rhythm appropriate to the needs of the body.

There is no way of predicting exactly how that unrestricted pattern or rhythm will look. All that we can be certain of is that, as we surrender the weight of our body to gravity, our pattern of breath will begin to shift. If it doesn't, then our surrender to gravity is probably only partial. At one moment the breath may speed up significantly; at another it may slow down to the point of becoming scarcely

---

6) It should be emphasized that this gradual shift in our pattern of breath is a natural by-product of our surrender to gravity. It cannot be forced. It has long been observed that states of mind, the gesture and structure of the body, and patterns of breath are mutually interdependent, and that any alteration to any one of the elements of this triad will automatically affect and alter the other two. Of these three, the pattern of breath is the easiest to manipulate and alter. Consequently, a wide variety of techniques that focus primarily on breath as a means of affecting our psychophysiological conditioning have been developed in different schools of growth and transformation down through the centuries. While the actual techniques, as well as their intended effects, often differ dramatically, they all take advantage of the transformative power of the breath. In the system of pranayama, for example, the student is instructed to manipulate the breath in a variety of different ways, each of which is capable of producing a distinct physiological response. Almost all the different forms of Reichian therapy use a forced and exaggerated breath to generate sensation and emotion. All of these techniques can be valuable in assisting a body's attempts to heal itself. They are curative in nature. However, they are not meant to be normal breathing patterns. A full-bodied pattern of breath involves no element of control whatsoever. It is simply the natural breathing pattern that occurs in a body that is both balanced and relaxed.

detectable. The volume of air that we inhale may increase dramatically and stimulate a strong energetic response in the body. Alternately, we may find that we come to a place at which the breath almost stops and the body becomes numb. The possibilities are endless, and the patterns, if yielded to, will keep on transposing themselves, sometimes from breath to breath.

Over time, the breath will settle. A soft, shimmering current may pervade the entire body, binding it together as a unified field of tactile sensation. At this point, an interesting phenomenon begins to occur; the tactile awareness of the body fuses with the experience and flow of the breath. Whereas formerly our awareness of breath was confined to the organs of respiration proper, now it is as though the whole body has become the organ of respiration. The more we are able to touch upon this quality of breath, the more we open to a force that stretches us gently from the inside, cleansing the body of residual pain and blockage.

The inhalation can now be felt to expand outward from the area around the navel in a domino effect, reaching simultaneously to the top of the head and the bottom of the feet. We become at once both lighter and more grounded. With the exhalation, we retrace this movement back into our navel, back into our center of gravity. After a pause, the process begins again to repeat itself millions of times until our final exhalation. Every inhalation gives birth to us anew. With every exhalation the being or mind state that existed during that breath passes away.

The Buddha clearly observed the strong interconnection that exists between breath and states of mind. The whole of his practice was based on the continuous observation of what is actually happening in the present moment. Breath is with us every moment of our lives, and it makes an excellent object for observation. Even today in southern Asia, as well as in many schools in Japan, breath continues to be the preferred focus of meditation practice. The meditator is instructed simply to remain observant of the passage of breath without manipulating or forcing it in any way. As we merge more and more with the rhythm of inhalation and exhalation, we gradually free ourselves from automatically identifying with the contents of our minds. We move from the periphery of our awareness back again into our center. At our core, we encounter and become more fully rooted in the full-bodied ground of tactility, the full-bodied ground of being.

"As you breathe in, breathe in with the whole body. As you breathe out, breathe out with the whole body." These were the Buddha's instructions. Like a call and its echo, reverberating across time, it is remarkably similar to Ida Rolf's observation of how breath moves through a structurally integrated body. It comes from a different place and time. It was revealed through a different process of discovery, and yet the sentiment is fundamentally identical. The Buddhist focus is on balancing the mind; the somatic focus is on balancing the body. Both, however, provide support for the other. By surrendering the weight of our body to gravity, we make the pattern of breath that the Buddha refers to possible. By becoming more aware of the process of breath, we become more aware of our body's tactile nature and its relationship to gravity.

Stillness and Movement

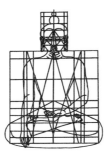

"*To harden into a Buddha is wrong.*"
Ikkyu

C ommon to all forms of animal life is the presence of motility. From the simple functions of an amoeba's single cell to the complex arrangement of cells and tissues that make up the largest vertebrate mammals, everything is in motion. The presence of movement in the body of an animal indicates the presence of life. If ever that motion should stop, it is a sign that the animal is dead, and its physical body begins to decay. From the point of view of the extension of life, motion has an absolute value.

From the point of view of our journey toward flowering, however, just the opposite would appear to be true, at least on the surface. "Be still, and know thyself," suggests the psalmist in the Old Testament. Almost every spiritual tradition, in both the East and the West, espouses a similar sentiment. Stillness of mind, the silencing of the incessant clatter of our internal monologue, is perceived as the necessary precondition for self-knowledge. Only a quiet mind can know itself. Only a quiet mind can gain access to the "still, small voice" inside. Coupled with this focus on quieting the mind is the bringing of the body itself to a condition of stillness as the means of experiencing inner silence. This is especially true within Buddhist traditions that emphasize the value of sitting meditation.

In the life of a human being, however, silence and stillness are relative terms at best. If we go into the desert or enter into the rear chambers of a deep cavern, we begin to appreciate the rich musicality inherent in silence. No matter how silent our environment may appear to be, there is always sound. The high-pitched frequency of our nervous system, for example, can become almost abnormally audible in a quiet place. In a similar way, there is no such thing as true stillness of the body. The degree of motion may vary from moment to moment, but the presence of motion never does. On a cellular level, everything is in a state of constant movement, even in moments of supposed repose. On a more apparent level, the action of breath keeps the body constantly, if subtly, moving. In addition, there is always the rhythmic thumping of the heart. Absolute stillness and silence do not exist within life forms.

Stillness implies quiescence; it does not imply stiffness and rigidity. This is especially important to remember when we advocate stillness as a value in conjunction with spiritual practice. When we begin observing ourselves, we are often struck by the unnecessary amount of verbal chatter we engage in and the extraneous motions that our bodies half consciously perform. Our need to verbalize may manifest as an actual ongoing dialogue with another person, or it may appear in its unspoken form as our persistent, internal monologue. The extraneous motions that our bodies make may range from nervous ticks and habits of which we are unaware to more noticeable movements, activities, and patterns of social behavior in which we regularly participate. The cause of these verbal and physical forms of extraneous expression is our inability to accept the body. By quieting our voice and mind, and diminishing the amount of unfocused physical motions in which we regularly indulge, we dramatically encounter the experience of our body. If we can yield to the current of this experience, we remain quiescent. However, if we become stiff and rigid in our attempts to bring about this quieting and stilling, we unwittingly succeed in fueling the momentum of the merry-go-round that we are so desperately trying to get off.

Stiffness and rigidity create further imbalance in our body and confusion in our lives. By holding our body still, we interfere with our natural pattern of breath. Forced stillness stirs up waves of mental chatter that convincingly lure us into the illusion that there does, in fact, exist an egoic entity from whose mouth these waves of chatter issue. As we become more balanced, the unbridled momentum of our internal monologue begins to slow down. In this calmer state we see that our thoughts do not emanate from a single, substantive source, but rather appear and disappear sporadically, like shooting stars blazing across the evening sky. Appearing out of nowhere, they disappear just as quickly, leaving no substantive trace. With this kind of realization we move closer to a true understanding of the stillness referred to by the psalmist.

When resilient patterns of movement and breath become more natural, we gain greater access to ecstatic, flowering states. When we learn to emerge from our hardened shells, we enter into a life of perpetual motion; here, paradoxically, is where we find the source of inner stillness. Continuously animated with both subtle and obvious movement, the body becomes vibrantly fluid and open. The immobility and lack of coordination that cause painful pressure to build begin to soften. We become more graceful in our movements. In effect, we come out of our condition of stasis, and it is to this coming out or emergence that the word "ecstasy" literally refers.

Sitting

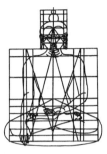

You should not be tilted sideways, backwards, or forwards. You should be sitting straight up as if you were supporting the sky with your head. This is not just form or breathing. It expresses the key point of Buddhism. It is a perfect expression of your Buddha nature. If you want true understanding of Buddhism, you should practice this way. These forms are not a means of obtaining the right state of mind. To take this posture itself is the purpose of our practice. When you have this posture, you have the right state of mind, so there is no need to try to attain some special state.

Shunryu Suzuki, *Zen Mind, Beginner's Mind*

Standing, sitting, lying down, and moving about--the body knows only these four basic themes, and every position, posture, or gesture that we can assume is a variation on one or more of them. By about one year of age we have learned how to sit, stand, and walk. For the better part of our lives we spend our hours of wakefulness with our spine erect and upright, perpendicular to the plane of the earth's surface and more or less in line with the directional pull of the gravitational field. When we lie down to rest and sleep, this relative positioning is reversed. The body now becomes aligned with the horizontal plane of the earth and perpendicular to the line of gravitational flow. For our species, then, it would appear that wakefulness and alertness are a function of the spine's verticality. As it becomes more difficult for us to remain upright with ease, our awareness becomes duller and increasingly cloudy. Finally, we give in to this condition which we call fatigue and lie down to rest. Our lives move back and forth in the manner of an alternating current between sleep and wakefulness, between the horizontality and verticality of the spine.

The relationship between sleep and wakefulness has often been used as a metaphor to describe the process and goals of spiritual practice. Mistaking our concepts of what is real for reality itself, we move through life like sleepwalkers. We manage not to stumble, but we have little or no awareness of what is actually happening to us. As our preconceived notions drop away and we come to experience the constituents of reality more directly, we begin to "wake up." In the terms of yet another associated metaphor, we come out of the darkness that is so necessary for our sleep and experience a luminosity that allows us, even forces us, to see things as they are.

Every position and gesture of the body can facilitate this passage toward greater wakefulness. By far the most common position that has been traditionally chosen for this purpose, however, is the sitting position. In many ways sitting is the perfect meditative posture. Lying down can be too passive and moving about too active a posture to support a balanced inquiry into the nature of things. Lying down most often gives way to further sleep and internalization; what we call the external world ceases, for the time being, to exist. The activity of moving about can so draw us out of ourselves that we focus almost exclusively on the objects of the external world and tend to be less aware of what might be called our inner world, the process of our minds and our bodily sensations. Sitting lies somewhere between these two poles and partakes of both. It allows us to be both restful and alert, and it is on these two qualities that the success of our meditative inquiry primarily depends. Relaxation and awareness in balanced combination with each other generate a powerful catalytic effect on the process of meditation. Progress is much slower when either is lacking.

Because we are, by nature, animals of activity, most meditation practices instruct us to "do" something while we are sitting. It may be:

* Paying attention to the passage of the breath as it moves in and out of the nostrils or causes the abdomen to rise and fall.

* attending to the ongoing process of mind and emotions

* observing the ever-changing sensations of the body

* listening to the inner sounds of the body

* visualizing a particular image in exacting detail

* silently repeating a word or phrase

* working with an unsolvable riddle in an attempt to arrive at an "answer."

The varieties of meditational practice are extremely diverse, and yet there is a denominator common to all of them which cancels out their superficial differences. This common theme is so apparent that it is easily overlooked. It is the sitting posture itself. At the most obvious level, what seated meditators are doing is sitting. If a person, unfamiliar with meditation, was to observe a group of seated meditators, each engaged in one of the different practices mentioned above, he or she would most likely report that the people were all doing the same thing. While different techniques may attract different types of people, it is tempting to conclude that the benefits of practice have less to do with the technique itself than they do with the simple fact that meditators spend long hours familiarizing themselves with balanced sitting. This is made clear by the following story:

"And it is said of Master Dogen (the founder of the Soto sect of Zen whose sole exercise consists in sitting), that when asked his opinion of the method practiced in the Rinzai sect, he answered, 'Very good, very good.' 'How so?' the other asked. 'They practice the *Koan*, don't they?' (the solving of an insoluble riddle). 'Well,' said Master Dogen, 'there may be people who can sit still only if they have something to think about. However, if they achieve enlightenment that way it is not thanks to their thinking but to their sitting still.'"[7]

Teachers of all traditions of meditation stress the importance of keeping the spine comfortably erect and the back and neck in a reasonably straight line. If our upper body can assume such a position comfortably, the process of meditation unfolds on its own. If we are unable to come to balance in this way, our task becomes much more difficult. The clarity of mind that long hours of sitting meditation can reveal is a natural by-product of a body that is balanced around a vertical spine. Interfere with that natural balance, and the resulting tension generates further superficial patterns of mind-stuff.

Just to sit in a position free of tension is one of the most potent bodily gestures that we can assume. Yet most of us do not know how to sit in this way, especially for long periods of time. Our sitting posture is generally either collapsed or, if we are making a special effort to "sit up straight," filled with tension and resistance to gravity. In a collapsed posture the back becomes rounded and overly elongated, and the head inclines forward and down. The front of the body shortens, and the abdominal viscera become compressed. If, as in the case in certain Buddhist schools, this collapsed and casual posture is not allowed, the student may assume an overly rigid posture in his or her attempt to sit properly. The head may be held up and back, the chin tucked in and down. The belly may be forced to protrude, and the hands held in a particular position which may not feel natural but which is, nonetheless, considered correct and proper. The result, much like the standing military posture, is a body filled with tension and restriction. While the collapsed posture encourages a feeling of sluggishness, the overly rigid posture can cause the mind to become highly agitated. They both interfere with the energetic flow that results from a deep meditative state.

It is relatively easy to sit in either a posture of collapse or a posture of rigidity. What is truly difficult is to find the balancing point between these two extremes, the place at which our upper body is not only erect and vertical, but also extremely relaxed. To sit in this way is one of the most elusive and demanding of all the physical actions our species can attempt. Yet it is almost as if the entire purpose and thrust of our evolutionary course is compelling us to become ever increasingly adept at this act of balance. As a species, our bodies have evolved unfalteringly in the direction of greater verticality. This move has been accompanied by an extraordinary

---

7) Karlfried Graf von Durkheim, *Hara* (London: George, Allen & Unwin, 1962), p. 143.

expansion in the development of our brain and nervous system. Anthropologists used to believe that a growth spurt in the brain preceded the moment that our ancestors lifted their front legs from the ground and stood balanced on their back legs alone. The discovery in 1974 of an early hominid skeleton nicknamed "Lucy" has opened the possibility that the expansion of our brain size actually followed, and was perhaps even made possible by, our shift to a two-footed stance. The movement toward expanded consciousness is, in our species, a function of verticality. The states of mind that an advanced meditator may touch upon are dependent on a heightened condition of verticality and balance. These states may, therefore, be seen as a preview of the naturally occurring consciousness of our species at a time in the future when we have perfected our evolutionary imperative toward a full and effortless verticality. While we obviously have a long ways to go, it is nonetheless a heartening prospect to contemplate.

Our ability to sit in a position that is both vertical and free of tension depends on a variety of structural factors. To understand these factors it is helpful to begin by considering our customary sitting posture and how our furniture reinforces this configuration.

The sitting posture that our culture perceives as comfortable is a posture of collapse (Figure 2). Virtually all of our furniture--from sofas to car seats to "easy" chairs, and even to rigid, supposedly "straight-backed" chairs--is designed to allow and encourage this posture. Three major structural relationships typify this posture:

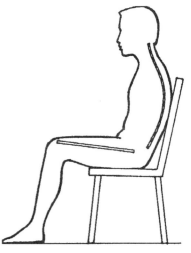

Figure 2.

1) Most of the weight of the upper body falls well behind the pelvis and sitting bones.
2) The knees often occupy a spatial position that is higher than the sitting bones.
3) Consequently, the front of the body shortens and collapses relative to the exaggerated length in the curving arc of the back.

It is this third structural relationship that causes us so much difficulty, but if we are to alter it successfully we must begin by modifying the other two. What we are trying to create is a structure in which the abdomen, thorax, shoulder girdle, neck, and head can line up vertically in relationship to one another and, as a whole, rest directly over, or even a bit in front of, the sitting bones of the pelvis. Check how you are sitting right now as you read this. Most likely, the line of your upper body will be positioned quite a bit behind your sitting bones. When seen from the side, the spine will appear to angle back and away from an imaginary vertical until you reach the neck and head segments which appear to come forward in compensation. If you examine the angles at which the seat and back of the chair on which you are sitting are situated, you can begin to appreciate how our furniture encourages our body to assume this postural configuration.

It is the relationship between the height of the knees and the sitting bones that largely determines how easy it will be for the upper body to situate itself comfortably atop the pelvis. A configuration in which the knees are elevated above the level of the sitting bones causes the top rim of the pelvis to tip backward. As an immediate consequence the lumbar spine must also shift backward, counter to its natural curvature, and the upper torso has no choice but to collapse over its base of support. If the knees are beneath the level of the sitting bones, the pelvis naturally assumes the position that gives optimal support to the upper body. The lumbar spine moves forward, and the rest of the body follows accordingly.

With this kind of relationship established, it is a relatively simple matter for the torso of a structurally integrated body to balance over the pelvis. Correct posture is achieved with minimal effort. With practice, this sitting position (Figure 3) can become just as natural as the more conventional posture of collapse. It allows a person to sit comfortably for longer periods of time and is much more effective in promoting an overall sense of clarity, alertness, and wakefulness. The body will experience much less overall strain, and there will be a great deal less cramping and restriction of the internal organs of the torso.

In the traditional posture of meditation the meditator sits down cross-legged on the floor. The crossing of the legs, in conjunction with a balanced pelvis, can provide a very secure and stable base of support for the upper body. It can also cause a great deal of strain in the joints of the legs and in the lower back. Consequently, it is very important that a meditator learns to sit in such a way that minimizes strain.

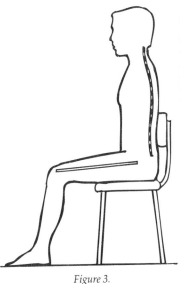

Figure 3.

One of the guiding concepts of Buddhist practice is the cultivation of self-reliance. The student comes to realize that he or she no longer needs to depend on unnecessary external aids and supports to provide satisfaction. Many serious meditators fall into the trap of taking this concept to the extreme and choose to sit on a hard, flat surface with little additional cushioning and support for the knees and pelvis. Almost without exception, their bodies fall into a posture of collapse, since it is not possible in this position for the sitting bones to be elevated high enough above the knees to give the upper body the support that it requires (Figure 4). It is possible for a person to sit on the floor in this way and pull the upper body forward and up into a position that appears straight. However, appearance by itself is not at all our goal. Such a posture is antithetical to a condition of surrender and can only be maintained for long periods of time through a great deal of effort. If the meditator were to relax the tension that secures the verticality of the torso, his or her body would immediately revert again into a posture of collapse.

It makes much more sense to elevate the pelvis by sitting on a firm supportive cushion. Every meditator will have to experiment with this until he or she finds the height and density of supporting cushion that works best. A cushion that is too low will not provide adequate support for the upper body. A cushion that is too high will cause the top of the pelvis to tip so far forward that the body will become swaybacked, and a great deal of strain will be felt in the lumbar spine. Depending on the person's weight and the surface of the floor or ground on which he or she is sitting, it may also be helpful to place the cushion on top of a broad supportive mat to provide greater comfort for the ankles, legs, and knees (Figure 5).

Many of us will begin a meditation practice with bodies that are not as flexible as they might be. This is especially true of older people. If the cross-legged posture causes too much distortion in the body, if the strain in the joints of the legs is too severe, or if the knees are unable to touch the ground easily, a meditator may instead choose to experiment with a kneeling bench or simply sit on a chair. Once again it is important to find the height and angle of seat that best suits the individual body. What works for one person will probably not work as well for another, and we should also keep in mind that over time, as the structure of our body continues to shift, it may be necessary to make additional adjustments and refinements to our arrangement of supportive cushioning.

When beginning a sitting meditation practice, it is helpful to choose a technique that has a specific focus, such as the passage of the breath or the sensations of the body. Such a focus can inject an element of form into what can otherwise be an often highly amorphous experience. The breath

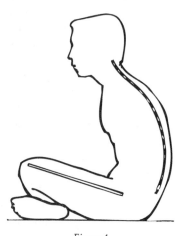

Figure 4.

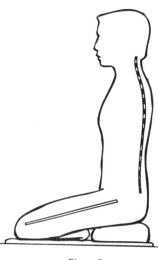

Figure 5.

and the sensations of body are always present, so if we ever become lost in a confusing maze of thoughts, fantasies, or strong emotional swells, it is relatively easy to refocus our attention on these ever-present aspects of reality and find our way back to the present moment. Over a period of time, as we familiarize ourselves with the process of meditation, our focus may naturally broaden and deepen. Until we have come to a highly balanced position in our sitting and can experience the whole process of body and mind as a unified field, however, it is better that we continue to focus on a single, isolated object.

By working in this way, we begin to gain a deep insight into the ongoing process of our own body and mind. Over long hours of sitting we will feel highly pleasurable sensations slowly fade and pockets of pain and tension emerge, only to melt away again as well. Periods of great clarity in which we become intensely and exclusively concentrated on the object of our focus will alternate with periods of confusion. During these moments we may become so lost in the narrative of our minds that it becomes almost impossible to hold onto our chosen object of focus.

This alternation between relaxation and clarity on the one hand and tension and confusion on the other will become the recurring theme and dynamic of our meditational experience. Our work is not to try to manipulate this process, but simply to come to balance and allow the process to unfold in whatever manner it chooses. Consequently, we must be careful not to bring expectations to our practice of sitting, but instead to cultivate an attitude of acceptance that is broad enough to embrace any experience that may arise. Sometimes the mind becomes very quiet, or we may feel ecstatic flows of energy in the body. If we become attached to these experiences, we make things difficult for ourselves during those moments when the mind fills with endless narratives of anger or fear, or when the experience of the body becomes mostly one of pain or numbness.

Our meditation experience will keep spiraling back and forth, as layer upon layer of *sankharas* (the accumulated residues of past holdings) come to the surface and are released. When a *sankhara* that causes us great difficulty and agitation is released, a wonderful feeling of calm will often appear in its wake, and the body will feel profoundly balanced and whole. While it may be tempting to perceive this afterglow as the goal of the practice, it is simply half of the process, no more or less important than the other half, the very experience that generated so much discomfort and confusion. And as the process continues, this feeling of calm will also gradually fall away, and most likely the next level of deep *sankharas* will begin to make its appearance in the form of physical pain or an agitated mind.

An image that is helpful in describing this ongoing process is that of peeling away successive layers of an onion. If you remove the outer brown covering, the onion appears shiny and moist. Now set the onion aside, and after a day has passed that very same layer will have dried out and become hardened and brown. It, in turn, is now ready to be peeled away. Surrendering to gravity has a similar effect on our body and mind. It can allow layers upon endless layers of deep *sankharas* to make their way to the surface of our awareness and, when the time is ripe, to drop away. If we try to force this process, if we attempt to speed it up in any way, we only succeed in obstructing it. If we cling to the pleasurable openings and resist moving into the discomfort that may arise, we interfere with and block the process. In short, we become stuck.

Many of us, when we come to realize that the condition of our lives is much like that of sleep, attempt to force ourselves to wake up. But we wake up by consciously and fully allowing ourselves to experience the depth of our condition of sleep, not by forcing our eyes to open wider. True aliveness can only be found by moving deeply into our sense of numbness or dullness. Within the core of our experience of pain, and nowhere else, do we find the seed that can sprout into ecstatic experience. Although our task would appear to be to dismantle the rigid and hardened structure that manifests as egoic mind, we must be very gentle in dealing with that quality of mind. Only through accepting and owning up to our sense of separation can we allow it to fall away.

For many people, the goal of meditation is the cessation of involuntary thinking. Certainly the endless train of thoughts, observations, and fantasies that form the narrative of our inner monologue gives rise to much confusion and nurtures many of the erroneous notions we hold about ourselves. Yet one of the common mistakes we can make is to regard that silent chatter in a negative way, to relate to it as an adversary that needs to be crushed and eliminated. As hellish as it may sometimes seem to us, our unconscious chatter is nonetheless an expression of the purest vital energy, albeit in a body that does not allow that energy to flow through it freely. The Buddha never said anything about forcibly stopping the process of thinking. The third truth of his teaching simply describes a condition in which our attachment to thought lifts and an unexpected clarity of mind is revealed. The cessation of surface mental patterns is only one of the many attributes of this condition of mind. If we can properly cultivate an attitude of acceptance, we can begin to view the progression of thoughts that appear and disappear as impersonally as the sounds that present themselves so fleetingly to our ears. In this way we become less identified with the thoughts that fill our minds. The veil of thinking begins to lift on its own. Fighting with the process of thinking in an attempt to curtail it creates tension and can only lead to further entrapment within the very domain of the mind from which we seek release.

In summary, it is possible to speak of three distinct components or phases of sitting meditation: balance, awareness, and acceptance. The posture of balance allows the meditator to surrender the weight of the body to gravity. In this position we can begin to allow the ever shifting experience of body to emerge fully into our field of awareness. We can allow our breath to assume whatever pattern is appropriate at that moment and allow for that pattern to change. If we allow the presence of body and the pattern of breath to manifest without interference, we maintain our balance. If we try to alter or control our pattern of breath or react to any of the sensations of body that may appear, we bring tension into our posture and block the natural unfolding of the meditative process. Once the posture of balance has been established, the meditator may choose to focus awareness on a particular object or experience. Such a focus helps ground us within the reality of the present moment as we traverse the often disorienting terrain of the meditative landscape. The chosen object is most often an isolated aspect of experience such as the passage of breath as it moves in and out of the nostrils, but it may gradually broaden to include the full spectrum of body and mind.

The first two components set the stage for the third as the dialectical drama of mind begins to unfold. The attitude of acceptance allows us to maintain equanimity in the face of the formidable ebb and flow of the meditative process. As ever deeper layers of *sankharas* gradually appear on the surface of the mind and body, they get released if we do not react to them.

As this drama proceeds, our sense of balance changes. Through experiences of profound release our body automatically moves into new and more refined dimensions of balance. We may feel expanded and elongated. In such a buoyant state our posture becomes stable and secure. As these experiences pass and less pleasant states of mind and body take their place, our sense of balance will once again become less certain. By working with the very same principles of structure with which we began, however, we are able to weather these inner storms much more easily than if we must constantly struggle to remain erect. From one pole of experience back to the other, the act of balanced sitting reveals to us the deeply therapeutic face of gravity.

Gravity Dance

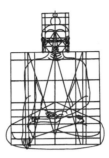

If you bring forth what is within you, what you bring forth will heal you. If you do not bring forth what is within you, what is within you will destroy you.
The Essene Gospel of Thomas

During the nine months of gestation prior to our entrance into the world, we float as if weightless, suspended in the waters of our mother's womb. At birth our environment changes drastically. The earth itself becomes our maternal ground, and we remain inseparably bound to it throughout the whole of our life by the umbilical cord of gravity. Not until death, when our matrix of experience undergoes another drastic shift, can that cord be conceivably severed. Gravity is our constant partner in the dance of life. The whole of our life is spent in its embrace. It is up to us, however, to determine whether our relationship with this partner exhibits grace and playfulness or is weighted down with tedium and travail. When a fiddler strikes up a tune, some of us join in eagerly, others of us go through the motions clumsily with little apparent enthusiasm, and still others withdraw to the corners of the room as if we could disappear into the shadows. All of us, however, are players in the dance.

No two snowflakes are alike, and no two bodies are identical. We are of the same genus as everyone else on the planet, and yet by virtue of the limitless variations in human structure we are all unique. Consequently, the way we dance in life is unique. No two people will walk or sit in quite the same way. No two people will express themselves identically. Our bodies have evolved to enable us to perform an almost unlimited variety of physical movements. We live, however, in a society that tends to minimize or discourage physical expression. In compliance with what is considered to be acceptable behavior, our movements within the public domain are limited to a fraction of the movements our body is capable of performing. The problem, of course, is that our bodies are designed to be highly mobile, flexible, and expressive as is evidenced by children at play. Our bodies want to move. Our bodies want to play. Our bodies want to dance in their own unique way. By restricting our range of movement, we diminish our awareness of bodily sensation. As this awareness recedes, we become even more awkward and limited in our movements and expressions. We lose our uniqueness, and our dance begins suspiciously to resemble that of our neighbors.

So we stand muted, our arms hanging expressionless at our sides. Just as we have lost touch with the darkly rich and sensuous world of our bodily experience, so too have we forgotten the way in which our body wants to move and express itself. Neither, however, remains lost to us completely. Not only can both be rekindled, but the rediscovery of either one strengthens the reemergence of the other. As we become more familiar with the experience of our body's tactile presence, we become more flexible and graceful. Our movement quite naturally becomes more expressive. If we focus on unearthing the long-buried movements that our body wants playfully to engage in, we ultimately uncover a deepening awareness of areas of bodily sensation that we have long forgotten or perhaps never even knew existed.

The form of dance that we are talking about here is completely personal. It will look different for each one of us. There are no specific steps or movements that can be taught. There is nothing that can be practiced to perfection. The rhythm that our body responds to as we begin this dance does not come from any external source, but from deep within. Listening carefully to the experience of our body, we can discern a tempo arising from the deepest cellular level. It is to this inner rhythm that we must give response.

The key to reviving this dance in ourselves, like so many things in this book, is our experience of the gravitational field. Our relationship with gravity is our constant guide in the practice of sitting meditation, and this practice can be seen as the passive expression of this dance. The movement that we experience as we sit in meditation is almost entirely internal. Various pressures and sensations arise and pass away in the body. On the screen of our minds is projected the ongoing drama of our desires and aversions, our hopes and fears, our fascinations and obsessions — everything that ordinarily lies hidden in the distantly obscured recesses of our psyche. The motion and speed of this internal dance can at times become dizzying, and yet the stability of the sitting posture allows us to maintain our balance. We become the calm at the center of a tempest.

The standing posture is another matter entirely. Those few square inches where the soles of our feet contact the earth provide us with a highly precarious base of support. Just as the slightest wind causes the tallest of trees to sway and shudder, so too does our standing posture invite motion. Rather than being a posture of rest, it demands resolution through movement. Rarely do we see someone standing still of their own volition for an extended period of time. If we are forced to stand idly in a line, waiting to be seated in a restaurant or received by a bank teller, we become edgy and impatient. Our body can learn to sit still in comfort and repose, but we do not want to stand still for very long at all.

To initiate this dance, then, all that you need do is stand. In the beginning it will be helpful to do this in the privacy of a closed room or in a place out-of-doors where you will not be disturbed. As you continue standing, feel as if you are giving in as much as possible to the field of gravity. As you keep letting go in this way, relying on the buoyant effect of gravity to hold you erect, the body may begin to sway slightly as it spontaneously makes minor adjustments necessary to maintain its balance. As you continue to stand in this way, you will become increasingly aware of the different sensations in your body. Areas of which you normally have little or no awareness may present themselves noticeably. You may feel stiffness or pressure as you encounter parts of your body that seem to hold back, as though refusing to surrender to the gravitational field. As your awareness of these places of holding deepens, the body may spontaneously begin to stretch in response. It is through these slight swayings and gentle stretchings that your dance begins.

Once it has begun, it is self-propelling. All you need do is keep on listening to the information your body is sending you in the form of tactile sensation, and then let your body respond to this information as naturally and unselfconsciously as possible. In the beginning the movements may be soft and subtle, resembling the yawning and stretching of a cat as it comes out of sleep. It is an appropriate image as our body, like the sleeping feline, is awakening to itself. No one knows where the dance will take us. It may remain soft and gentle, or it may become broadly, even harshly, expressive. As the pace of the dance accelerates and gains momentum, gestures and movements may become much more pronounced. At times it may come to resemble formal styles of movement: the flourishes of traditional ballet, the contained power of an age-old martial art, the lengthening motions of hatha yoga. At other times it may look like the inflamed desperation of a person possessed. No one can dance this dance but you.

The progression of this dance, just as with the practice of sitting meditation, will often be marked by alternating gestures of expansion and contraction. These alternating expressions are the pulse and heartbeat of the dance, the systole and diastole. Each in its turn allows for the expression of the other. Through gestures of tension, contraction, or shortening the dance enables us to uncover and explore areas of deep energetic blockage. By willingly moving into these places, we set up the possibility for release and expansion. As an area of deep chronic holding releases, the gestures of our dance shift. The movements of our body become much more relaxed, expansive, and extended. Our pattern of breath will often change as well, becoming much fuller and freer. In the wake of this release the next layer of contraction will gradually begin to reveal itself, and the cycle begins anew as the body once again slowly contracts down on itself. The progression of the dance must remain as natural and spontaneous as possible. It cannot be forced. If your energy wants to move and expand, you allow it. If your energy wants to contract and withdraw, you allow it. The dance must be allowed to dance itself.

Many of the gestures that develop during the successive phases of the dance may seem unfamiliar and abstract. Others, however, may resonate deeply within you. They may kindle feelings of recognition and long-buried acknowledgement, as though you were encountering a long lost acquaintance. Each gesture or movement may suggest a specific character or attitude, many of which will be familiar to you as different aspects of yourself. During the systolic phase you may encounter sad characters, fearful ones, buffoons, ruffians filled with hatred; the list is endless. It is not uncommon during the diastolic phase to uncover characters of wisdom and strength, beings of enormous innocence, fragility, and beauty. All of these characters, taken together, form the pantheon of your personal mythology. They are all different facets of yourself, different masks that you put on and take off as the situation requires. Each one is dependent on a different physical posture, a different pattern of holding or release. Their source may be an incident from your own life, or they may stem from the common repository of human experience to which each of us, even if only dimly perceived, has personal access. If you can allow them to emerge onto the stage of your dance, they will gradually dissolve over time, relinquishing and making available the energy that they hoard. If you don't allow them expression, they will withdraw back into the shadows of consciousness where they silently exert influence over you.

If we are sincere in wanting to let go of something, we need to bring it fully to our awareness. If we truly wish to drop something, we need first to hold it firmly in our hands. Otherwise we do not have anything to release, and our efforts become futile. Some of the gestures that appear in our dance may seem awkward and unsightly, and some of the characters that emerge may seem unpalatable or offensive. For this reason we often try to keep them hidden so that no one, ourselves included, may come to know about them. But this strategy does not work. Unexpressed, they cause stagnation. Something in us withers. If we can allow them expression, no matter what form that expression takes, the situation becomes workable. Out in the open they reveal themselves. Like a light-sensitive molecule exposed to the penetrating rays of the sun, they undergo a transformation as the bonds that sustain them begin to give way.

And so the dance proceeds from one character to the next until we have familiarized ourselves with them all. This process of mythic unfolding can have a wonderfully healing and purging effect. Each character is dependent on a fixed expression or posture, and it is this fixity that the dance effectively dissolves. Fixity and holding are manifestations of fear, the signs of a body out of balance. They cause us to shrink away from life. Fluidity and motion, on the other hand, indicate a positive, accepting involvement in the contents of our lives. They are the mark of a body at ease with itself and its environment. What manifests through a balanced body does not form itself into a fixation. It simply comes and goes, leaving no mark, and accumulating no residue. Such a body is not limited in its repertoire of expression. It can allow for the expression of the whole spectrum of human emotions without having to react to any part of it with aversion or clinging. It is this reaction that fixes these expressions of emotion and turns them into distinctly familiar characters over time. When the hold that these characters have on us loosens, our bodies are able to remain fluid and maintain a balanced state for longer and longer periods of time. As they finally recede like actors relinquishing the spotlight, they are replaced instead by a presence of great silence and extensibility. Only on such an empty stage can we begin to discern the nature of our true identity. Only then is our identity unmasked.

In the beginning it will be helpful to set aside specific periods during which you can experiment with this dance. Over time, however, we come to realize that our dance comprises the whole of our lives. At any given moment we are either cooperating with the energetic impulses that appear in our bodies or interfering with them. Every time we choose to cooperate it is as though we chip away at a small section of the self-created dam that keeps us stagnant and congealed. We remove the obstacles that separate us from the rich vitality and virile flow of our life force. The effect of our dance will be slowly accumulative. Over time the sense of stagnation will lessen, and the dam will become more transparent and penetrable. Our stiffness and rigidity will begin to soften and thaw. If we could get out of our own way, our body would bring us back into balance.

Path and Goal

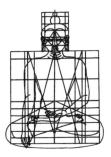

*E*quanimity — the evenness of mind that accompanies an attitude of acceptance — is the true indicator of balance. The ability to remain equanimous in the face of any situation that may arise is a more accurate measure of our progress toward balance than is the appearance of any particular type of sensation or the creation of any particular configuration of structure. It is relatively easy to maintain this clarity and evenness of mind when our body is highly balanced and we experience a stream of unified, subtle vibrations passing through us from head to feet. What happens, however, when this phase passes, and a whole new layer of tension begins to emerge? The body loses the ease of relative structural balance, and the process of mind becomes increasingly chaotic and confused. It is during this phase that the equanimity we have cultivated is truly put to the test. Do we react with struggle and aversion, or are we able to accept and observe this phase of experience as easily as the one that preceded it? As we have seen, struggle and reaction interfere with the process of unfolding; they only prolong this phase of confusion. If we can accept whatever is occurring with the knowledge that it will eventually pass, the release at both a structural and mental level will occur far more rapidly. Equanimity propels us along our intended path. Out of an attitude of balance even greater balance is born.

How does this relate to the signs of balance that were outlined in the first chapter: alignment, symmetry, and resilience? Applied to the structure of the human body, these indicate specific configurational relationships and patterns of movement which can be viewed as undeniable somatic goals. So specific, in fact, are these signs that it is easy to construct an image of these goals against which we can measure our progress toward balance. Just such images can be found within both the Buddhist and somatic traditions. The image of the Buddha sitting in meditation

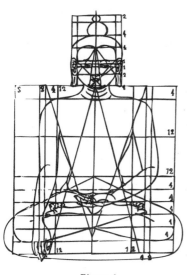

Figure 6.

(Figure 6) is drawn according to a specific and exacting canon of proportions that has been handed down through generations of Buddhist artisans and iconographers. It may not be a realistic portrait of the historical Buddha's actual appearance, but it is undeniably a potent tool for instruction. In the words of Boddhidharma, the first Zen patriarch: "The essence of things is not describable; to express it words are used. The royal way that leads to perfection is not marked out; in order that initiates may be able to recognize it, forms are used."[8]

The image of the sitting Buddha is just such a form. Its purpose is to instruct and inspire the practitioner in a way that words alone are not capable of doing. The Buddha was a being who came to be known for the supreme balance of mind that he was able to attain. What is made explicit through this image, however, is that such an exalted mental state is dependent upon a heightened condition of physical balance. For the beginning Buddhist student, the initial instruction to "sit with the spine straight and the body relaxed" may or may not be understood in a way that allows the student to translate that instruction into experience. When this instruction is presented in the form of a visual image, however, the student can more easily understand what is being suggested. It becomes much easier to embrace and embody the instruction.

The somatic image of refined balance (Figure 7), viewed alongside the contrasting image of the same body before undergoing treatment, is taken from photographs of a child with whom Ida Rolf once worked. Even though a condition of structural balance is the evident goal of this particular form of somatic intervention, the image suggests that such a shift in physical structure brings with it a sense of well-being that no amount of somatic theory could as effectively express. The Buddhist goal is a balanced mind. The image of the sitting Buddha, however, tells us that this goal is somehow a function of balance of body. The somatic goal is a balanced body. The Rolfing logo, however, leads us to understand that a sense of well-being follows this goal like a

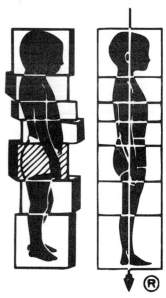

Figure 7.

---

8) Titus Burckhardt, *Sacred Art in East and West* (London: Perennial Books, 1967), p. 132.

welcome shadow. Each goal is dependent on the other; each goal in turn reinforces the other.

Both images (and the traditions from which they emerge) approach the issue of balance from opposite directions. Both imply that there is something valuable in bringing the body to a condition of balance. Neither image, however, is able to convey the intensely personal nature of the path of unfolding that allows such images of balance to become reality. Verticality and balance, in both traditions, are *not* goals or ends in themselves. They are necessary preconditions that allow an attitude of surrender to enter into our lives. Through this attitude of surrender the force of gravity becomes a powerful therapeutic agent capable of transforming the way in which we experience both our body and our mind. To this end Ida Rolf often spoke of what she called the "gospel of Rolfing: When the body is working properly the force of gravity can flow through it. Then, spontaneously, the body heals itself."[9]

A body can begin to work properly only when it is able to experience itself exactly as it is, with nothing added to or subtracted from that experience. At every moment there is some sort of discernible sensation on every part of the body, even down to the smallest cell. The sum total of these sensations *is* our body at the experiential level. Normally, however, we are aware of only a small fraction of these sensations. The holding and tensing that typify a body in conflict with the gravitational field block out whole areas of bodily sensation from our awareness. By redefining our body's relationship with gravity, we are able to increase that awareness dramatically. In order for this to begin to happen, it is necessary for our bodies to become *relatively* ordered and balanced. It is not necessary for them to become *perfectly* ordered and balanced. Our initial focus and work is to achieve enough balance and verticality so that the body can begin to cooperate with gravity and experience itself as a decidedly tactile presence. From this place the natural unfolding that we seek has no choice but to begin. From here the process of healing initiates itself; as it proceeds, our bodies spontaneously become more balanced, vertical, and at ease. In this light the goal of any somatic practice can be seen as providing a person not so much with a body of perfection as with a body of participation.

Difficulty arises if we forcibly try to make the structure of the body conform to an image of supposed perfection. In doing so, we misperceive our true goal and enter instead into the trap that S. N. Goenka, a contemporary Buddhist teacher, calls "the game of sensations." We can forcibly manipulate our experience in hopes of reaching a desired end, but more often than not, all we succeed in doing is fueling the dual attitudes of craving and aversion that are the source of our misery in the first place. Such an attitude overly values some experiences and denigrates others. We lose our equanimity and, with it, our ability to uncover and nurture the balance that we seek. Furthermore, no one structural image, no matter how convincing or

---

9) Rosemary Feitis, editor, *Ida Rolf Talks about Rolfing and Physical Reality* (New York: Harper and Row, 1978), p. 31.

attractive it may appear, can adequately capture the experience of balance. Balance is a dynamic condition, an ongoing process in which the subtlest structural compensations follow one another with great rapidity. It is highly misleading to conceive of balance as a perfected, static condition which can be attained and then maintained. Such a conception does not take into account the role of resilience, one of the major marks of balance. Without resilience, a body becomes rigid and stiff. Held in an apparent expression of balance it remains as bound and limited as a body in conflict with gravity. Chains of gold can keep us imprisoned as effectively as chains of iron.

While an image of balance may symbolically express or indicate a certain kind of experience, we must arrive at that experience by allowing it to emerge naturally rather than attempting to manufacture it. We come to true verticality and structural balance by bringing awareness to the body and then surrendering to gravity, not by forcing ourselves to straighten up. We then begin to perceive our body as an energetic field of tactile sensation whose relative openness or blockage largely determines its most habitual structural pattern. As our awareness of these sensations increases, we observe that the sensations themselves change. When they do, the structure of the body begins to shift accordingly, on its own. If we can give in to this process without reservation and allow it to move us however it wishes, it may take us into postures, gestures, and expressions that have nothing at all to do with the images of balance that we are familiar with. If we remain attached to these particular images of structure as a goal which we must strive toward and then maintain, we severely limit our ability to surrender in this way. It is one thing to be guided and inspired by the image of a goal. It is quite another to become so consumed by that image that we manipulate our experience in an attempt to create the appearance that the goal has been reached. The very impulse that initiated our journey will then begin to block its progression. Significantly, when our energy does come to rest after episodes in which we have allowed even the most unusual gestures and expressions to move through us, we find that our body has become more balanced. It has moved closer to an approximation of what we perceive to be ideal structure.

Equanimity is the mechanism that allows us to perceive as perfect every step we take along the path of unfolding. Moments of disorientation and confusion in which the mind is unsettled and the sensations in the body are painful, gross, and intensified may be every bit as prevalent as periods of joyful release. Reaction of any kind simply blocks the momentum of our progression. An object that is placed in a swiftly flowing river will eventually arrive at the larger body of water into which that river empties. Along the way it may encounter tumultuous rapids, deep pools of great calmness and clarity, and long stretches of almost imperceptible and uneventful motion. If we react to the unpleasant aspects of our journey, if we cling to the intensely pleasurable insights that are bound to appear, or if we lose interest during the interim moments, we interfere with the natural pace of the process of unfolding and postpone the arrival at our destination.

All we need do is contact the path at its beginning. The path itself, if nurtured and tended with the same kind of loving care we bestow upon a garden, will then propel us to our goal. Some form of therapeutic intervention will often be necessary to help a person contact the path at its beginning. Once the path has been contacted, however, it may be more appropriate to augment the therapeutic intervention with a form of practice that we can engage in on our own. Therapeutic strategy is the way of the West; the strategy of practice is most commonly found in the East. Both serve an important function.

The goal of therapy is to reveal and then dissolve the structural, attitudinal, and emotional-energetic blockages that keep us from contacting the path. The goal of practice is to insure that once having contacted the path, we do not lose it. Without some form of therapeutic intervention we may never be able to find our way onto the path in the first place. Without some form of ongoing practice, our efforts may never bear fruit. With their many different techniques for the common goal of rekindling an awareness of the body, all the different forms of somatic work attempt to bring us into contact with what we have called the path of unfolding. The messages of verticality, balance, and surrender become our personal guides as we proceed on our way into progressively unfamiliar territory. Equanimity—born out of a thorough understanding of the cyclical nature of this process—gives us the perspective that is necessary to insure that we continue moving in the right direction.

Sound, Vision, and the Components of Reality

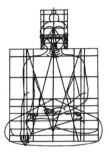

The eye and visibile objects; the ear and sounds; the nose and smells; the tongue and tastes; the body and sensation; the mind and mental objects or ideas.
Buddha, *The All*

S o far in this book we have focused almost exclusively on our sense of touch as the medium through which we can most easily familiarize ourselves with the experience of body and with the understanding which that experience can reveal. While touch is the primary and most obvious sense through which we are able to do this, all of the other senses play significant supporting roles. Our body has a sound to it as well as a feeling, and certainly we are aware that our body has a visible shape and form. All of these sensory fields, if we attend to them carefully, speak to us of our own changing nature and impermanence.

If we direct our hearing to a place in the center of our head, we can begin to hear what our body sounds like. At first we may only be aware of a rapidly oscillating, high-pitched frequency, but as we patiently and sensitively continue to listen, a whole host of other sounds may appear. Some of these sounds are identifiable: the transmission of impulses throughout our nervous system, the beating of our heart, the pulsing movement of our bloodstream, the inhalation and exhalation of breath. Others are more difficult to label with any certainty. As our awareness deepens we may uncover a surprising array of sounds, all of which contribute, like different instruments in an orchestra, to our inner symphony. The ability to tune in to this inner world of sound affects us in much the same way as does the ability to experience the complete range of sensations that fill our body from head to foot; it heals us and helps establish balance. This music is, in fact, the sound that a relaxed and balanced body naturally emits. A body filled with tension can generate, and consequently be aware of, only a much more limited range of sound.

We are constantly surrounded by a sea of sounds. However, just as we have only a partial awareness of the tactile presence of our body, so too are we ordinarily aware of only a fraction of these external sounds. Sometimes when we lose touch with the experience of body and become lost in the monologue of the mind, it is helpful simply to turn our attention to sounds as a way of becoming grounded again. Sounds are constantly changing, and so it is difficult to get stuck anywhere. By attending to the changing pattern of sound, we free ourselves from the hold of our mind. The inner narrative becomes less prominent. As it loses its momentum, it will be replaced again by a deepening tactile awareness of body. It is not possible to be caught up in mental chatter and to be aware of the world of sound at the same time. The reason for this may be that sound is closely related to our sense of tactility (through which we most directly apprehend the experience of body) by virtue of its connection with our "inner ear," the mechanism in the body that regulates balance. The medium through which sound expresses itself is, furthermore, remarkably similar in texture to the medium of tactility. Both are clearly vibratory in their mode of expression, and both can only be fleetingly apprehended as their components appear and disappear with astonishing rapidity. The same, of course, is technically true of the other two major sensory fields, vision and mentality.[10] However, these other two fields reveal the truth of their changing, vibratory nature much less noticeably than do the fields of sound and touch.

If we look at our body, what do we see? Our conceptions of reality may shade and affect our perceptions to such a degree that it becomes very difficult to experience the visual field directly without this accompanying conceptual overlay. Mostly we conceive of our body as a static entity, much like an image in a photograph. Consequently, we tend to see bodies (and to experience our own) as having distinct edges with little mobility. However, if we look closely and carefully, we find that this is not at all the case. Even if we were to sit very still, the constant activity of our respiratory and circulatory systems generates a subtle but constant movement within the body. With every breath, our body expands and contracts. With every heartbeat, a pulsating wave — similar to the ripples that move across the surface of a pond into which a small pebble has been recently dropped — passes through the body. The cerebrospinal fluid surges and recedes as much as ten times a minute. And if we become deeply relaxed and gaze softly at a portion of our body, we can detect a much finer and even subtler activity as well. We can actually see the pulsating, vibrational current of life which, on a purely tactile level, we experience as the stream of very minute and rapidly dancing sensations that fill the body from head to foot. Confronted with this perception of reality, we are forced to drop our

---

10) Western psychology acknowledges the existence of five distinct sensory fields: vision, sound, touch, smell, and taste. Within traditional Buddhist psychology the field of mentality is considered the sixth, and final, sensory field. This field includes all of the objects that we associate with mental functioning: our ordinary process of thought with its predominantly linguistic basis, emotional states, dreams and intuitions, and the process of awareness itself. Including mentality as a sensory field, rather than a separate aspect of experience, has the significant advantage of limiting the distinction we ordinarily make between our inner world and the outer world we perceive through our senses.

notion of the body as a solid mass with distinct, hard edges. The image that emerges in its place is dynamic and vibrant; it has an appearance of motility that more accurately resembles a freshly unearthed bed of ladybugs or a solar storm.

Life is movement and constant change. This movement, in all its varying speeds and intensities, can be seen as directly as it can be felt or heard. Such perception is in no way special or extraordinary, but is simply the natural experience of a balanced body. Tension and holding interfere with the highly sophisticated mechanisms of the body's sensory systems and alter the appearance of the data that they are designed to receive.

Our eyes are often referred to as the gateway to our soul. If we look into someone's eyes we can almost immediately learn a great deal about that person. We are able to pierce through their surface mask and perceive quite directly their hidden fears and joys, the pain and aspirations that they rarely reveal. And if that person holds our gaze and looks back at us, an energetic circuit is established that enables us to see deeply not only into the other person, but into ourselves as well. By holding each other's gaze in this way, we encounter the tactile experience of our own body, sometimes so strongly that we may feel the need to avert our gaze or to laugh as a means of interrupting the energetic connection that we have established with the other person. This technique can be an enormously powerful method with which to experience the body and dissolve the barriers that exist in conventional social interaction. To enable it to work effectively, both participants must be willing, as much as possible, to continue holding each other's gaze and to accept without manipulation whatever sensations, emotions, thoughts, and perceptions emerge as a result of the contact. It is not uncommon to experience strong tactile sensations, a variety of different emotional states or roles, and a certain amount of visual hallucination. As you continue to interact in this way, a great deal of repressed mental and emotional material will come to the surface and resolve itself; energetic blockage and restriction will also be felt to dissolve. After a period of time, the body will begin to feel strangely refreshed and balanced. The mind will experience both an increased clarity and a lessened identification with its surface contents.

One of the most powerful and beautiful encounters of this kind occurred in the year 1244 when the renowned Sufi teacher and originator of the dance of the whirling dervish, Jallal-el-din Rumi, met a wandering seeker named Shamsi Tabriz. Very little record of what transpired between these two exists, but it is known that when they first met, they encountered each other's gaze and Rumi felt his mind beginning to melt. The two then went into seclusion and spent three months together. Almost certainly they kept looking at each other, allowing the barriers that keep us from flowering and from experiencing our true identity to drop away. When they emerged from their retreat, they were as one being, immersed in an ecstatic intoxication familiar to the Sufi tradition. After such a meeting, two people are never again the same, and their understanding of the meaning of friendship is forever altered.

All of our senses reveal a similar vision of a world that is constantly shifting and changing from one moment of awareness to the next. This world is incredibly rich and varied and yet essentially empty of any enduring substance that might be identified as "I." For a variety of reasons, however, it is our tactile sense that best reveals the truth of this vision. We are far less familiar with our sense of touch than we are with our other senses. Paradoxically, we are able to use this situation to our advantage. Because of our relative inexperience with the world of tactility we are better prepared simply to observe bodily sensation as it is. So familiar are we with vision and sound that it is difficult to have a purely visual or auditory experience without immediately labeling or interpreting what we see or hear. Compared with these senses, we are still relatively unsophisticated in the range of labels and interpretations that we have created to describe our bodily sensations. Our tactile vocabulary is limited to the most generalized expressions of feeling; in comparison, we have an almost limitless number of words to describe what we see or hear. This allows us to remain more firmly rooted in the experience of tactility than in the experience of our other major senses. Furthermore, focusing on our sense of touch forces us to observe and embrace the experience of our whole body. Nerve endings that are sensitive to tactile impulse pervade the entire body, while the nervous receptors of our other senses are confined to the area of our head. Our sense of touch, then, brings us into contact with the experience of our entire physical body. Our other senses relate only to a small portion of that body.

Rekindling our awareness of the stream-like, vibratory nature of the body is an essential factor in establishing a vision of reality that is both accurate and honest. Such an awareness provides the foundation or ground on which the successful perception of this vision rests. To this end, our first task is to focus our attention exclusively on the body, to close our eyes and ears for some time and to allow the ramblings of the mind to recede into the background of our awareness. By doing this, we can come to appreciate the body as a distinctly tactile presence. Once our awareness of this presence has been established, we can then begin to open to and embrace the other sensory fields with much less danger of becoming lost, stuck, or confused. If we are able to remain grounded in the experience of body, it becomes much easier to see and hear what is in front of us without immediately labeling or interpreting it. We can observe the passage of thoughts that move through our mind without unconsciously grabbing after some and pushing others away.

Ordinarily, we tend to think of physical sensations and thoughts as residing exclusively within the domain of the body while visual objects, sounds, tastes, and smells are aspects of the world that we conceive of as external to ourselves. This distinction between our inner and outer world is a deeply pervasive one. It is largely responsible for the concept we have of ourselves as isolated entities moving through time and space. So conditioned are we to thinking of most everything we see or hear as existing somewhere "out there" that we hardly ever stop to question whether this is an accurate assumption. Most people, when faced with the hypothetical problem of determining whether a tree falling in a forest makes any sound if no one is present to hear it, will finally conclude that while certainly *something* has transpired, it cannot accurately be labeled as a sound. The experience of sound, rather, depends on a variety of factors. First there must be a source of vibration that oscillates at a frequency accessible to our auditory system. The tension that is released as the trunk of the tree breaks apart, brushes against its still standing neighbors, and finally strikes the ground, provides these elementary vibrations. Equally important, of course, is the presence of a person at a close enough range to hear what is occurring. The final element required is consciousness directed toward sound. I may be sleeping nearby or so involved in a train of thought or so absorbed in the examination of a visual object that the tree may fall undetected.

It becomes much more difficult to accept the conclusions of this kind of analysis when we apply it to objects within our visual field. Somehow we believe that objects look the way we perceive them to look whether we are looking at them or not. We believe that visual appearance is an intrinsic property of objects, independent of the mechanism of the human eye and the consciousness that allows us to view them. However, if no one is there to observe it, does a tree falling in the forest look like anything? Does it exist as a visual event? Much more reluctantly we are forced to conclude that the question applies to vision as well as sound. In spite of a rich array of interacting vibrations that can be detected by the human eye, nothing intrinsically visible has transpired if that eye is not present. Nothing is visible without an eye to see it; the visible world appears as it does only because we are looking at it. The world that I perceive from moment to moment does not exist somewhere "out there" separate from "me." It requires, rather, my active participation in the co-creation of its appearance. It is as intrinsic a part of me as are the ever-changing sensations of my body and the thoughts in my mind!

By taking this observation a step further, we are forced to expand greatly on what we understand to be the actual perimeters of body. Ordinarily we mark those perimeters as the outermost surface of our visible form. Everything that exists within these perimeters is "me;" everything that exists outside of them is "not me." The problem with such a definition is that it is based on an incomplete survey of the information that is available. It is based on our sense of vision and mentality, but excludes our sense of touch. It is, furthermore, a reflection of the primacy of the egoic mind. In its passion for analysis and dissection, the egoic mind would like us to see ourselves as separated from everything outside of the perimeters of our physical body and is powerful and tenacious enough to insure that what we do "see" supports this understanding.

Already we have seen that our understanding of what marks the outer limits of the body changes as soon as we shift our focus to our sense of touch. By observing the body as a tactile rather than a visual phenomenon, the visualized limits of our body begin to soften significantly. Where our body begins and ends is no longer as distinct as it once was. The softly vibrating presence of body can be felt to extend well beyond where our eyes tell us the limits of those parts should be. We may also experience that the world of tactility possesses a spaciousness that does not necessarily correspond to our conventional understanding of geometrical space. When we concentrate on a certain part of the body, for example, we may encounter a feeling larger or more spacious than we know that part to be. On other occasions, our bodily experience may become microscopically compressed, as though we were filling only the tiniest point in space.

Add to this the information we receive through our eyes and ears, exactly as it appears without the addition of any conceptual interpretation, and our understanding of what constitutes the perimeters of body takes an exponentially expansive leap outward. In a heightened state of balance, the whole of the visual and auditory fields that we perceive comes flooding through the doorways of our eyes and ears and penetrates, quite dramatically, to the very core of our being. Through direct experience, then, we recognize the world we perceive as an extension of the self, just as our arms and legs are extensions of the axial trunk of the body. I can *conceive* of a world outside of myself and develop an entire science to explain and substantiate this conception, but the world that I *perceive* from one moment to the next is nothing but an integral part of myself. Put more simply, everything that I see or hear exists inside my body! This is not to say that the *objects* that I perceive exist inside my body, but that the moment-to-moment *perceptions* I have of these objects certainly do.

Such an experience of embodiment bears even less resemblance to the form of the physical body with which we began. The portion of my visible form that I can actually see is simply one of many objects that, taken together, form the whole of my visual field. It is the visual field seen in its totality that becomes the visible aspect of what we are now calling "body." The crucial shift in perspective that we are establishing here is from a largely conceptual vision of reality to one that is a more accurate reflection of immediate experience.

An ever-changing mosaic of sensory elements constitutes the whole of my experience. Foremost among these elements are vision, tactility, sound, and thought. Smell and taste, while embellishing the mosaic, generally play less prominent roles. Every one of these sensory fields can be viewed as an individual system, a complete universe of its own. All of these systems interpenetrate and overlay each other to create our perceived image of reality. In much the same way, the color separations made by a printer, when combined, blend with one another to create the overall printed image. When balanced, we can be simultaneously aware of all these elements. At any given moment I can be aware of the entire tactile presence of my physical body. I can be aware of the changing patterns of the entire fields of vision, sound, and thought as well. I can bring even greater depth to this experience by including the subtle presence of taste and smell. In all their different aspects and changing forms these elements, like building blocks of an interlocking puzzle, make up the whole of my experience. Nothing that I can experience exists outside of this collection of six elements.

What am "I," then, in terms of this vision of reality? My conventional understanding is of a being separate from the rest of existence. But within this multilayered vision of reality there is no such separation; what exists instead is a rich interpenetration of sensory fields that, taken together, form my experience of embodiment. Sounds change from moment to moment. Thoughts, emotions, and different states of consciousness come and go. If I look carefully at the objects in my visual field, they all seem to shimmer very subtly and rapidly. If I turn my head to one side or the other, many of these objects disappear while others appear to take their place. The sensations in my body are constantly changing at different rates of appearance and dissolution. Smells linger for a moment, and then are gone. The same is true of tastes. Everything is in a condition of constant flux. Within this kaleidoscopic awareness, my sense of "I" has no place of reference or support, no unmoving ground on which to stand and stabilize. What I become, rather, is the enormously spacious *context* in which all of the ever-changing *contents* of my immediate experience play themselves out. Such a contextual experience of myself, while extraordinarily rich and full, is essentially without enduring substance. The reappearance of "I," this sense of myself as a substantive entity that dwells inside my physical body and endures at least as long as my physical body survives, occurs only if I attempt to shut down any of the aspects of this vision. I can withdraw my consciousness from the visual field. I can block out sounds or not feel the sensations in my body. But by doing any of these I go unconscious. I put a limitation on the potential for experience that any given moment possesses. In such a condition of unconsciousness, I conceive of myself as an entity separate and distinct from the rest of reality.

When we first began exploring the body, we worked to bring the right and left sides into a more approximately symmetrical balance and to achieve greater integrity in the relationship of the major bodily segments. Expanding outward from our conventional vision of reality, we are now challenged to balance and integrate whole sensory fields. A printer can create an accurate visual image with just four colors: red, yellow, blue, and black. To arrive at this image, he makes up four separate plates, one for each of the colors, and passes the paper over each of these plates. If only two of the colors are used, the image will be hazy or indistinct. If one of them is far too strong or weak, the image will also appear inaccurate. The printer will have to readjust the intensities of the colors and balance them out to gain the desired result. In much the same way, if we wish to create an accurate vision of reality, we need to include and ultimately balance out all the sensory fields. A vision of reality that is based on thought and vision alone is highly distorted. By adding the elements of the other sensory fields, and allowing them to imprint themselves simply as they are, without any interpretative filtering, our vision of reality comes into clear and vibrant focus, and our distortions drop away.

When we begin to focus our attention in this way, what we will probably first become aware of is how relatively imbalanced the sensory fields are in relation to one another. We may be lost in thought with only a limited awareness of tactility, sound, and vision. Our attention may be so fixed on a visual object that we have little awareness of the play of sound that is present. If we are extremely hungry, we may become so engrossed in the taste of the food we are eating that very little else seems to exist for us at all. For a printer, it is a relatively easy matter at this point to adjust the intensities of the colors and achieve the desired image. For us, however, the process of resolution happens not so much through conscious manipulation of the various sensory fields, but through acceptance of them as they are. In much the same way as we work to dissolve a pocket of painful sensation in the body not by forcing the sensation to change but simply by accepting it as it is, so too can we balance out our awareness of these fields by accepting them as they are. Acknowledge whatever imbalance may be present; see clearly that certain ones do, in fact, predominate over others. These fields are present all the time so we do not need to force them to appear. Acknowledge the fact of their presence, no matter how indistinct that presence might be. Through a gradual and patient focusing of awareness, the relative imbalances will naturally settle themselves out, and the vision of reality that has been alluded to in this chapter will come into focus. If we attempt to force this vision into focus, we will only bring tension into our body, and such a condition of tension does not permit us to perceive things in this way.

Our ability to perceive this vision of reality is directly paralleled by the degree of balance and relaxation in the physical structure of the body. More specifically, it is a reflection of the accomplishment of one of the last and most difficult tasks of integration that we are faced with as we work to balance the body: getting the head to sit effortlessly on top of the rest of the body. It is very common for people who enter into a program of somatic therapy to report that they experience a major split between their head and the rest of their body as though the two were not functioning cooperatively at all. We perceive what we conventionally label as "the world outside" through the sensory receptors of the head. What we call our "interior world," the domain of experience that exists within or just at the boundaries of our physical body, is perceived through our senses of touch and mentality. We know that the sensory receptors for our sense of touch pervade the entire body. We are not so clear as to where our experience of mentality is located. Certainly our brain is cradled within the protective walls of our cranial cavity, but it is in direct contact with the whole body via an extraordinary maze of nerve fibers. While we think of language and thought as emanating from the area of our head, strong and unexpected emotion can be felt to erupt from deep within our pelvis, stomach, or chest. When we include areas of our mind where language and thought don't play a prominent role, we find that the total domain of the mind occupies a space approximately identical to the shape of our body. In other words, our experience of what we call our exterior world is largely a function of our head, while our experience of our interior world is more a function of the whole body. If we wish to integrate our head with the rest of our body, we must also unify our interior and exterior worlds. This is exactly what this vision of reality accomplishes.

Two major difficulties will crop up and prevent us from appreciating the accuracy of this vision: our attachment to visual concepts about space and our reluctance to admit to an alternative understanding based on immediate experience. Our conventional geometry tells us that no two objects can occupy the same physical space, and so we go on dissecting the fabric of reality and confirming our notions of separation, isolation, and distinction. But in this renewed vision of reality there is only one space, the locus of experience, and all of the sensory fields occupy it simultaneously. The scene that appears before my eyes, even though I may be looking out unto the most distant star, interpenetrates and occupies the very same "space" as does the field of sensations that fill my body from head to foot. All of the sounds that I can hear occupy this space; so do the contents of my mind and any smells or tastes that may be present. To understand and experience this notion of space, we need to relinquish our passion for dissecting the sensory fields. Instead we must focus on the unity of these fields as they appear to us in the present moment.

This shift in vision takes us from a world which is disjointed and remote to one that is marked by a heightened sense of unification, integration, and the ongoing interplay of enormously rich and varied sensory fields. It is directly paralleled in Buddhist psychology in the distinction that is drawn between *samsara* and *nirvana* and in the understanding that what separates these two perspectives is simply a transformative shift in the way we perceive reality. *Samsara* is conceived of as the domain of suffering. Because we tend to perpetuate our suffering through our incessant grasping after and avoidance of objects that appear in our sensory fields, it is ordinarily identified with the world of sensory experience. *Nirvana* is viewed as our potential for flowering, the condition in which our pain and suffering drop away. Because our relationship with the world we can perceive through our senses often locks us into self-perpetuating samsaric patterns, *nirvana* is often thought of as a dimension somehow removed from the world of appearance. However, Buddhist teaching is very clear to point out that *nirvana* is to be found nowhere but within the condition of *samsara*.[11] Ultimately, the components of these two experiential states are identical. The only difference lies in how we relate to and experience these components. The very same information can reinforce our sense of separation and the suffering that follows, or it can reveal to us the truth of interpenetrating relatedness and the attendant ease that accompanies this realization. Depending on the perspective that we are able to adopt, the rich and multifaceted experience of our body can either multiply the burden of the pain we carry or present us with the opportunity to allow that burden to fall away.

---

11) Hence, the famous Buddhist dictum: "Emptiness is in the apparent form; the apparent form reveals the condition of emptiness."

Metta

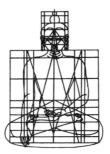

The path that the Buddha mapped for us begins with the objective acknowledgement of the discomfort, imbalance, and disorientation in our lives. Through a process of often painful self-observation and acceptance, we are led to perceive that everything that we can experience -- sensations, visual objects, sounds, thoughts, tastes, and smells -- is impermanent. Since everything arises eventually to pass away, we come to appreciate the futility of holding on to anything. Our awareness of impermanence deepens as we turn our attention to the experience of our bodies. What we may have originally conceived as a static mass with little or no sensation gradually begins to lose its unrelenting sense of solidity. In its place emerges an awareness of body that is highly dynamic in nature, and filled from head to foot with minute and rapidly changing sensations — a subtle but constant vibratory presence. Faced with the awareness of this stream-like presence of body, our concept of "I" begins to weaken and drop away, and a whole new panorama of experience opens up before us. Where originally we were limited by the vacuity of concepts and interpretation, we now find ourselves immersed in the richness of immediate experience. Starting out from a place of alienation and disjointedness, we have moved toward a condition which can only be called love. The Buddha called this condition *metta*.

Normally we think of love as the overwhelming attraction that we develop toward a specific person or object. The quality of love that we use the word *metta* to describe, however, is less selective in its focus. It is, rather, the acknowledgement of the deep connection and relatedness that pervades and binds together the whole of the universe, the unshakable feeling that everything is of one piece. Separation and distinction are workable concepts only in a world that promotes the attitudes of fear and distrust. To heal the pain that these attitudes generate and transform the alienation that we feel into love, it is only necessary to see that these concepts distort the truth of our immediate experience.

For example, I can distinguish as separate from myself and each other all the objects that appear at any given moment in my visual field. I do this through giving these objects names. The act of naming, however, removes me from the immediacy of experience. The world of experience exists, rather, at what Korzybski called the "silent level" — silent in the sense that it precedes the act of naming and classifying. If I am able to stay open to the visual field at the silent level, my experience will be very different from what it is when I view that world through the filter of concepts and progressive orders of abstraction. Dissecting the fabric of reality into a multitude of component parts spawns the notions of separation and division. Focusing instead on the unity of the fabric by remaining open to the wordless flow of raw sensory data generates great warmth, openness, and relatedness. Being able to contact this sense of connectedness greatly illuminates our lives. When we dismantle the mechanisms that blind us to the truth of immediate experience, the fear and sense of separation that these mechanisms foster disappear. Rightly seen as distortions of immediate experience, they are replaced instead by a feeling tone of love.

Love can only be found in the present moment. It is the binding agent that holds the various sensory fields together. It is the simple by-product of our ability to accept, without reaction, the data which these fields present us. Most of the time we attempt to manipulate this data, to alter it in such a way that we think will provide us with what we want. But through our constant interference we block ourselves from experiencing reality as it is, and so we bar our entrance into the domain of love.

When we lose awareness of the present moment we flounder amidst the random and often turbulent waves of our minds. We forfeit the richness and refuge of present experience and replace it instead with a running monologue of memories, fantasies, and hopes: the stuff of past and future time. Our thoughts about the future are riddled with fear and anxiety, even in anticipation of a pleasurable experience. Our thoughts about the past lock us into self-perpetuating patterns of guilt and discontent. Some memories are painful for us to recollect; others give us a momentary pleasure until we remember that the event exists no more. Our fantasies about the past and future are entirely the product of reaction. Images of what might have been and what hopefully may be obscure what is. Adrift in the mind, there is little room for love.

The data that appears in our sensory fields is the lifeline that can reconnect us to the present moment. It is to be found wherever we can focus our attention. All that we need to do is unconditionally accept the contents of our present experience: the visual objects, sounds, sensations, thoughts, tastes, and smells. Like a shadow, the feeling tone of love will follow automatically. If we lock ourselves into a pattern of reaction, however, it is as though clouds come out to blanket the sky, and even the traces of shadows become difficult to discern.

Unable to focus on an object or situation without reaction, we divorce ourselves from the richness and warmth of true *metta*. This is why it is so important in the beginning to refamiliarize ourselves with the experience of our body. Most of us have little awareness of the field of tactility, and yet it is there all the time. We block it from our awareness because the sensations to be uncovered are often painful,

onfronting, and difficult. By accepting the sensations of the body, we begin literally
o love ourselves. Only from such a base of self-acceptance and self-respect can
ve effectively extend our feelings of love outward.

The experience of love is too big for a single body to contain. It must be shared.
ist as it is difficult to accept the sensations of our body as we find them, so too
s it difficult to look at our friends and neighbors directly in the eyes. If we are
valking down a road and happen to look into the eyes of a stranger at the same
noment as the stranger is looking into ours, we will usually avert our gaze. Our
ear will not permit us to maintain the contact that our interest in each other has
roduced. By choosing fear in this way, we perpetuate our notions of separation
nd distinction and continue on our way. If we are able to look into another person's
yes and hold their gaze, a whole other set of conclusions reveals itself. In just a
w minute's time our conventional boundaries begin to soften, losing their hard
dge of distinction and opacity. The energy fields of our bodies, which people who
ave particularly sensitive vision can perceive as auras, slowly begin to merge, the
ne flowing into and out of the other. Once this connection has been established,
ur communication deepens, and the feeling tone of the encounter begins to shift
Iramatically. Like two objects that have entered a whirlpool and are both drawn
nexorably to its common source, our experience of ourselves and each other
radually merges and, at a very deep level, becomes indistinguishable. Such joining
ogether brings with it an awareness of the substratum of love that binds us together
s one body and from which each individual body emerges. The common lie that
ve share with the whole of humanity, our insistence on separation and isolation,
; revealed for what it is. By letting go of the fear that keeps us separate, we have
io choice but to fall in love.

Learning to love ourselves, acknowledging our commonness of experience, our
leep level of connection with everyone and everything on our planet and beyond,
iur lives become permeated with the fragrance of *metta*. What a long way we have
ome from the simple observation of the gravitational field and the effect that it
las on bodies! Like a strand of dominoes that have been lined up on end, we tap
he first one, and a chain reaction is initiated. One conclusion touches off another
nd then another until we find ourselves at a very different place of inquiry from
vhere we began. The implications of balance are very much like a strand of
Iominoes. Exploring the nature of our relationship with gravity, we are led to deeper
nd deeper awareness of ourselves and the world in which we live.

PART II:
The Experience of Balance

The Experience of Balance

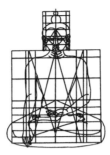

*T*he purpose of this section is to provide a variety of exercises that may prove useful as you begin to experiment with the ideas presented in the first part of this book. The alternative vision of reality that this book has attempted to convey is dependent on a shift in how we experience ourselves and our world. Each of these exercises presents a different strategy for understanding this shift. Each is designed to clarify a different aspect of the overall vision. As you begin working with them, you will see that, like pieces of a jigsaw puzzle, a successful understanding of any one of the exercises will offer clues to how the others fit.

Some of the exercises may prove immediately meaningful to you; others may not. When we begin to put a jigsaw puzzle together, we naturally focus on the most distinguishable landmarks such as the borders and major objects. After these landmarks have been established, the pieces that fill the spaces in between become more easily recognizable. Work with these exercises in the same way. Focus on the ones that you find useful; don't overly concern yourself with the others for the time being. As you continue to work with these exercises, a time will come when the awareness that each of them evokes will become a natural part of your life.

What was begun as a conscious exercise will be recognized as the natural expression of a body and mind in balance.

Whole Body

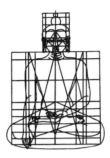

The ability to experience the body from head to foot as a distinctly tactile presence is the most important foundation on which an understanding of this alternative vision of reality ultimately rests. It is the lens that enables the perception of this vision to come into clear and vibrant focus. Without this ability, everything remains blurred and indistinct.

The field of tactility is our forgotten sensory field. At every moment there is a distinct tactile sensation of one kind or another to be found on every part of the body down to the smallest cell. Most of the time, however, we move through life oblivious to this richly detailed sensory web. Because our analogies of expression are most often couched in terms of the visual field (the most predominant of our sensory fields), we are inclined to describe this situation as being "blind" to the awareness of our body. It is more accurate, however, to say that we are "out of touch" with the experience of our body. The goal of this exercise is to get back in touch with this experience by rekindling our awareness of bodily sensation.

This exercise can be done anywhere, anytime, and in any bodily position. In the beginning, however, it will be easier if you lie down on a soft surface or sit in a comfortably upright position. After you have gained some familiarity with this exercise on your own, you can begin experimenting with it in more conventional situations with other people present. Certain circumstances tend to encourage an awareness of bodily sensation more than others. Experiment with this exercise in a variety of situations: at work, at play, at a party, in the presence of someone you love. The more you are able to bring bodily awareness into whatever you are doing, the richer that experience will become.

In the first part of this exercise, move your attention slowly and carefully, part by part, through the entire body. Be very precise and focused with your attention so that you leave no part of the body unexamined. Your task is to observe whatever type of sensation is present on the part of the body you are examining. The nature of the sensations that you may encounter can be extremely varied. You may feel heat in one part of the body, cold in another. You may feel burning or prickling sensations. You may come across an area of dull, aching throbbing, or you may encounter a softly pleasurable tingling. Some sensations may be extremely pleasurable, others quite unpleasant. Your task is simply to acknowledge the presence of all these different sensations. Try not to change or alter them in any way. As you continue to observe your body in this impartial way, the nature of the sensations will begin to change on their own.

To insure that you don't leave any part of the body unexamined, it is better to follow a specific order. Begin by bringing your awareness to the top of your head. Patiently observe this small part of your body until a distinct sensation of one type or another appears. As soon as this sensation has established itself clearly, you may begin to broaden your area of attention and, bit by bit, gradually survey the whole of the scalp area. Next, slowly pass your attention over all the parts of the face: the forehead, the eyes, the ears, the cheeks, the nose, the mouth, and the chin. Take your time as you do this. Degrees of sensation are extremely subtle and can only be distinguished by a calm and patient mind. Now move your attention from the top of your neck down the right arm until you reach the tips of the fingers. Survey each area of the arm separately: the shoulder, the upper arm, the elbow, the lower arm, the wrist, the front and back of the hand, and each individual finger. Move your awareness down the left arm in the same manner. Are the sensations in your left arm similar to the sensations in the equivalent area of your right arm, or are they different? If they are different, how do they differ? Now turn your attention to the front of your torso. Begin by focusing on the front of your neck, your upper chest, and your right and left breast. Move your attention past the area of your diaphragm and survey the sensations that appear in your belly area. Turn your attention next to the back of the torso. Begin at the neck, and slowly, vertebra by vertebra, rib by rib, move your awareness downward until you reach the coccyx. Expand the area of your observation to include the whole of the pelvis: the front of the pelvis, the back, the sides. Observe the sensations in your genitals and anus as well as the perineal space that separates them. Move your attention next through each and every part of your right leg: the different sides of the thigh, the area of the knee, the lower leg, ankle, foot, and toes. Do the same with your left leg.

Your attention should move slowly in the beginning, and your area of focus should be no larger than a few square inches. Be as precise as possible in your observation. See if you can detect subtle differences in sensations between adjacent parts of the body. See if you can determine where a specific sensation begins and ends. Depending on the clarity of the sensations you encounter, you may be able to move your attention fairly rapidly through the body or it may take a full half hour or even longer to complete one round. Once you have completed moving your awareness through the entire body, you may choose to reverse the order of your observation or move your attention once again to the top of the head and repeat the process a second time.

Common to all the different varieties of sensation that you may discover is the element of change. All of the sensations, if you observe them for some time, are seen to be constantly changing. Emerging out of nowhere, they appear for a moment on the screen of awareness and then disappear, only to be replaced by the next emerging sensation. This ongoing process of emergence and dissolution may occur with such rapidity that your mind can scarcely comprehend it except as a vague blur. At other times the rate of alternation can be painfully slow.

At first you may only be aware of sensations that exist at the surface of the body. Over time, however, you may be able to move your awareness into the core of the body, observing whatever sensations are to be found there as well. It is not uncommon, as you move your attention in this way, to encounter blind areas where there is no discernible sensation at all. The most effective way to deal with such an area is to allow your attention to stay on that part of the body for a slightly longer period of time. Wait to see if some kind of sensation will eventually emerge. You must be careful not to become impatient and attempt to force a sensation to appear. The purpose of this exercise is not to create a particular type of sensation in any part of the body, but simply to observe and accept the field of tactility as it is. As your awareness becomes sharper, you may even be able to acknowledge that the blank numbness of a part of the body where you don't seem to feel much is actually a kind of sensation in itself.

Having successfully activated an awareness of the tactile field of the body in this way, you can then move on to the second part of this exercise. Just as you can focus your attention on an isolated object in the visual field or soften and broaden your gaze so that you can perceive the whole of the visual field all at once, so too can you do the same in your observation of the tactile field. Now, instead of continuing to pass your attention through the body part by part, allow yourself to become aware of the whole of your body all at once as a unified, tactile field. At times the sensations that you experience may be quite uniform throughout the entire body, and it will be very easy to do this. At other times the sensations may be highly diverse and not at all uniform. At these times, alternate between the first and second parts of this exercise. Stay with the awareness of the whole body for a period of time, and then once again pass your attention through each and every part of the body. Having done this once or twice, again let your focus broaden so that you can be aware of the whole of the tactile field as a unified phenomenon. Just as each individual sensation is constantly vibrating and changing from one moment to the next, so too does the whole of the body, when perceived as a unit, appear to shimmer and pulsate in a dancing play of sensations. Being able to experience the whole body as a shimmering unit of tactility brings with it a pronounced feeling of relaxation. In the beginning it will be helpful if you spend a minimum of thirty minutes when you experiment with this exercise.

Body and Mind

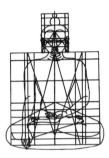

*T*he distinction between body and mind is a murky one at best. Certainly the experience of our body influences our state of mind. Likewise, any major alteration to our customary patterns of emotion and mentality will generate an almost immediate bodily response. The words "body" and "mind" supposedly refer to two separate dimensions of experience, but when we turn our attention to these processes and observe them carefully, the sharp lines of distinction fade.

One of the primary focuses of spiritual practice, as suggested in the second yoga sutra of Patanjali, is to calm the waves of the mind. One of the central premises of this book is that it is chronic tension in the soft tissues of the body that creates (or, at the very least, accompanies) these waves of mind. Rarely do we have moments when the endless narrative of the mind -- our running commentary of perceptions, aspirations, fantasies, past memories, and future projections -- stops completely. Depending on the nature of its contents, this narrative may sometimes be no more intrusive than a mild background hum. At other times, however, it can reach a volume that overshadows everything else that we might experience. Mild physical tension causes surface ripples to appear in the mind. Chronic tension at the core level of the body puts the mind into turmoil.

When the body is in conflict with gravity, we are not easily able to calm the involuntary chatter of the mind.[12] If we are able to come to balance without exerting effort, the chatter of mind will diminish and fade. In its place will emerge a quality of consciousness that is naturally calm and clear. Our awareness of both the body's solidity and the hardened barrier of the mind's superficial activity begin to dissolve. They will be replaced instead by a shimmering field of vibratory sensations.

---

12) The possible exception to this would be superficial trance states that conceal the bulk of mentality through their concentration on a single aspect of experience. Ultimately, however, this is not a true calming of the mind, as people who enter into these states discover upon leaving them.

Any major structural imbalance will successfully conceal this awareness. Instead of a uniform stream of sensations passing through the whole body, some parts of the body will feel too little sensation present while others will feel too much. Where there is too little sensation the body will feel dull or lifeless. The area will be cloudy and difficult to perceive. Where there is too much sensation the body will feel pain. The area will appear overloaded, and it may be difficult to observe objectively without reaction. The consciousness of such a body will be filled with endless waves of involuntary thoughts. This half-conscious monologue successfully conceals all deeper aspects of mind.

To understand this interrelationship further it may be helpful to construct the following simple diagram. Within this diagram the words "body" and "mind" are used to describe the two poles of a continuum of experience. The line that previously separated body from mind now irrevocably links them together. Within this diagram the horizontal line represents our spectrum of experience:

On the far left of this line would be situated all events that we consider predominantly tactile, such as strong physical pain. On the far right of this line are to be found all those events that seem more exclusively mental: insights of a conceptual nature, for example, or language. Ordinarily these events are perceived as belonging to two aspects of experience so unlike one another that no common connection can be inferred. However, what the model presented here stresses is the single, common line of experience. Depending on where they fall on this line, some events may seem more physical than mental; the reverse is true for others. Certainly an experience such as the joy we feel on seeing a loved one after a long period of separation or the relaxation that we feel after exercise or play cannot be accurately positioned at either extreme of the spectrum. As you move closer to the middle, it becomes increasingly difficult to say that an experience is exclusively "of the mind" or "of the body." Distinctions drop away, and the tactile sense of body takes on a mental quality as though it is imbued with consciousness. What we formerly perceived as mental now appears to have a decidedly physical or tactile feel to it. This awareness is most powerfully operative just at the middle point of the spectrum. From a spatial perspective we would call this the point of balance, and this is, in fact, the operative mode of consciousness for a body that can come to balance, a body that does not have to hold itself up to maintain its erectness. If this awareness does not come to a person, then there is still some degree of tensing and resistance to gravity in at least some part of the body.

This lack of balance insures that experiences or events fall either to the right or left of center. Now, to a greater or lesser degree, we will distinguish some events as relating more to the body, others to the mind. In other words, it is holding in the body and the subsequent lack of balance that follows that create these concepts and this distinction in the first place. As we come to balance, there is no longer "body" or "mind." There is only experience.

You can play with these ideas first by focusing at random on any part of the body, observing the physical sensations that exist there. As your awareness of the sensations sharpens and becomes more precisely detailed, slowly begin to acknowledge that these sensations possess a quality of mentality unto themselves. It is as though that part of the body knows itself. Within the physical sensation itself is to be found an intelligence that does not need to rely on the so-called "higher" centers of the brain to sense its existence. As you extend your awareness to include the whole tactile field of the body, you may gain access to a deeper understanding of who and what you are.

Now turn your attention to the process of thought itself. First of all, see that different levels of thought seem to occupy different spatial locations within or around the body. The unconscious chatter of mind may be located in quite a different place from where we find our conscious process of thought positioned. Strong thoughts of anger or love may be located in different areas still. Try, as precisely as possible, to establish a physical coordinate for every one of these different processes of mind. Once you have pinpointed some of these, you can start working with them. There are physical sensations on every part of the body. However, when you locate an involuntary thought, perhaps deep inside the head or neck, you will notice that there is very little sensation there, that only thought seems to occupy that space. Allow the thought to continue, but begin to bring more awareness to the place where the thought is located. Very gradually, as your attention remains focused in this way, some kind of sensation may appear in this location. As it does, the presence of "thought" will begin to diminish. After a period of time it drops away completely, and what you are left with is a presence of physical sensation that is highly aware of itself.

Interestingly enough, the end point of each part of this exercise is the same. No matter whether we begin from body or mind, in each case the exercise moves our awareness toward the center point of the diagram. It is important as you do this exercise to refrain from manipulating your experience. If you try to force your bodily sensation to be conscious of itself or attempt to manufacture a sense of tactility that permeates your process of thought, you will miss the point of the exercise. Consciousness has a fundamentally tactile quality to it, so there is no need to try to force it to appear this way.

Embodied Presence

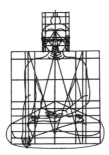

Ordinarily we go about our daily routines with little awareness of our body. Our daily activities may require us to focus carefully on the objects in our visual field, to listen attentively to the world of sounds that surround us, or to juggle concepts and words, but rarely do they require that we pay full attention to the tactile presence of our body.

As was suggested in the previous exercise, it is not possible to be lost in the semiconscious monologue of the mind and aware of the experience of the body at the same time. Either one of these conditions precludes the other's existence. During those moments when we become absorbed in the unwilled progression of thoughts that forms our internal monologue, we are literally not present. Oblivious to the potential wealth of information that the world is presenting through our other senses, we remove ourselves into the airy realms of past and future speculation. The purpose of this exercise is to make us aware of the condition of absence in which we so often find ourselves and to rekindle the experience of real presence.

The first two exercises have given us the ability to experience the whole of the body as a unified field of tactility. We are now in a position to take this recovered awareness out into the world. It is one thing to reconstruct this awareness in privacy; it is quite another to maintain it in the face of a constant barrage of sensory stimuli which we cannot limit or control. Moving outside the shelter of our homes into the world at large, we are bombarded by a dazzling array of sounds and visions, tastes, and smells. Often this bombardment becomes so intense that we relinquish our participatory sense of presence by retreating into the apparent shelter of our mind's internal monologue. However, this constant choice can only lead to an eventual feeling of impoverishment and constriction.

We may describe this condition as feeling disoriented or disconnected, as though we were walking in a dream. We may even come to view this disorientation as normal and forget that there are other choices available to us. The first part of this exercise, which can be done at random any number of times during the course of the day, is simply to become aware of how active our mind has become as we go about the business of our day. In terms of the diagram in the previous exercise it is an acknowledgement of how far to the right of center we have let ourselves wander in the present moment. Once we have acknowledged this to ourselves we can then begin consciously to expand our awareness to include a greater focus on the experience of tactility. This will have the effect of moving our experience back toward the center of the diagram. As soon as we are able to do this, we see that we have once again become more present. To experience this shift back toward the center it is not necessary to suppress the random activity of the mind. It is only necessary to redirect our attention so that we become more aware of the tactile sensations of the body. In just a few minutes time, as the relative ratio between mind and body evens out, the random mental activity will slow down automatically.

With patient and persistent practice you will see that you can include an awareness of your bodily sensations and presence any place and at any time. As you look at a scene in front of you or listen to sounds and words that are coming your way, you will see that your experience will have a different flavor or texture to it, if, in addition to the sounds and sights, you maintain an awareness of the tactile presence of your body as well. Absorbed in vision, simply allow yourself to be simultaneously aware of the unified field of your bodily sensations. As you attend to sound, allow that sound to penetrate and intermingle with this tactile awareness. This exercise requires a great deal of perseverance and practice before it becomes second nature. We have become so accustomed to not including an awareness of sensation as we look or listen, that it will be difficult to maintain this new attitude of inclusion for more than a few moments at a time. As it fades and we become once again more absorbed in the fields of either vision, sound, or thought, our sense of presence will fade as well. Once we acknowledge this withdrawal, we can begin again to shift our awareness back to the field of tactility. See if you can once again include your awareness of sensations as you look and listen.

In the beginning, it will be easier if you experiment with this exercise in surroundings that are familiar to you. Let yourself look at the wall of your bedroom. Can you maintain a simultaneous awareness of the visual image of the wall and the sensations of your body? Listen to the sounds in your neighborhood. Can your focus of awareness broaden to include not only these familiar sounds but the experience of your bodily presence as well? After you have gained a bit of familiarity with this exercise, you can begin experimenting with it in your place of work or as you walk down a city street. You will see that doing this exercise in public confronts you with the additional task of having to drop the customary masks that you put on whenever you move out into social situations. These masks depict the image of yourself that you want to project and are dependent for their expression on a great deal of holding and tension in the body. Consequently, they interfere with your ability to experience the sensational field of the body as it is. Only by letting these masks drop and fall away are you able to recontact the experience of your body as a unified field of tactility. As you continue to experiment with this exercise, you may come to realize that these postures or masks are not as vital to your social survival as you have ordinarily believed them to be.

Ourobouros

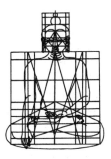

*T*he geometrical principles governing our inner and outer spaces are not at all the same. The *ourobouros* (Figure 8) is a Western alchemical symbol of integration. A serpent swallowing its tail, a straight line becoming a circle, it symbolizes the reconciliation of apparent contradictions. It can serve as a helpful, and at times even literal, metaphor for understanding these geometrical differences.

The experience of our body may have little in common with its visible shape and form. We may reasonably assume that the space that is defined by our bodily sensations should roughly conform with the physical shape of our body, that our tactile sensations should fit neatly into our bodily container much in the manner of a beverage in a bottle, but this is often not the case. Our conventional notions of geometry are largely based on our sense of vision. From this perspective we can clearly make out the physical shape and form of our body and determine with precision the outermost limits of that shape. If we switch our perspective to our sense of touch, however, the image of our body becomes significantly less distinct. From the perspective of tactility the image appears soft and somewhat amorphously shaped. Its edges become blurred, its outer limits uncertain. Not only does it become difficult to determine where our body begins and ends, but we may also find that tactile space possesses a fullness that seems incongruous in comparison to the limited form we had always visualized. It's as though a pint container is being asked to hold a gallon of matter. Although they supposedly describe an identical object, the two perspectives do not appear reconcilable.

Figure 8.
Ourobouros

This exercise will explore the spatial dimension of bodily sensations, permitting you to begin to appreciate how different this dimension is from our ordinary understanding of space. You may choose to lie down on a soft, supportive surface or sit or stand upright in a comfortable, balanced position. Begin, with your eyes closed, by bringing your attention to the experience of your body. Just as you did in the *Whole Body* exercise, move your attention slowly through each and every part of the body until you are able to feel a distinct, tactile sensation of one kind or another in each part. Once you have been able to stimulate an awareness of tactile presence throughout the whole body, shift your attention as precisely as possible to a place just at the surface of the body. As you keep on observing this part of the body, see if you can honestly determine where the outermost limit of your body actually is. Take your time as you do this. The longer you are able to remain focused on one little part of the body, the more clearly you will be able to determine what is actually transpiring there. Move at random to a number of other places just at the surface of the body, again attempting to determine where that part of the body begins and ends. When you feel satisfied with the results of your examination, shift your awareness to include the entire surface of the body. Once again, keep asking yourself where the limits of your body are located.

As you keep probing in this way, the spatial sense of your body may become highly distorted. You may find that the part of the body that you are examining may increase in tactile size, as ever greater areas of sensation are seen to be contained therein. From a purely tactile perspective, the image of our body mirrors our current image of a constantly expanding universe whose precise limits are unknown.

Once you have contacted this expansive feeling, allow your eyes to open suddenly and observe what happens. Are you able to maintain this very open and spacious feeling, or does the sudden inclusion of the visual field cause this feeling to recoil so that it once again fits neatly within the visible container of your physical body? If you find that this feeling of space automatically collapses in on itself as you open your eyes, let your eyes close again and allow yourself to recontact this spacious feeling. Now when you open your eyes, see if you can maintain this feeling for some time.

Most of the time our eyes function as receptors for visual information. We allow the visual field to come flooding into us. To maintain this feeling of spaciousness, however, it is helpful to reverse this customary visual polarity. We must imagine ourselves instead as a beacon of light that radiates outward through the passageway of our eyes, flooding our immediate environment with the light and energy we feel emanating from us. Sometimes it is appropriate for us to project our energy outward; at other times we need to be very receptive, allowing, even coaxing, whatever is occurring in our immediate environment to enter into us. There are no hard and fast rules to guide us here. If we remain open to the experience of the body, it will tell us what mode is appropriate at any given moment.

One of the most common difficulties that confronts us as we set out to explore the realm of bodily sensation is our unconscious expectation that tactile space and visual space should be identical. To this end we often try to manipulate our sensations to conform to our visual understanding of the space and shape of our body rather than just allowing the field of tactility to present itself as it is. Interfering in this way, it becomes very difficult for us to perceive the nature of this important sensory field with any kind of objective accuracy. As our awareness of bodily sensation heightens, the incongruity between these two spatial perspectives may become even further pronounced. In a state of extreme tactile dissolution, the experience of the body may bear no resemblance whatsoever to what we know the shape of the body to be. It may become difficult to distinguish with any precision from what part of the body a particular sensation is coming. What we know to be the right side of the body may be perceived as occupying a position in space somewhere off to our left, or vice versa. All that we can do during moments such as these is to acknowledge the accuracy of our perception, even though it may be presenting us with an image that is incomprehensible in terms of our conventional understanding of bodily appearance. Ultimately, the most effective way to reconcile contradictions comes through realizing that the simultaneous appearance of both is not necessarily an impossibility.

The final application of the image of the *ourobouros* is an even more literal one yet. Often, when moving our awareness through the body, we will uncover an area that appears almost as a focal point of contraction. It will inevitably feel as though too much sensation is concentrated in this one spot. Such a point may occupy a very small and specific place in the body, or it may appear to spread out and cover a much larger area. In dealing with a sensation like this it is helpful not only to probe the specific sensation calmly and attentively, but also to broaden our focus to include the parts of the body immediately adjacent to it as well. When we come across an area in the body that seems filled with too much sensation, it is very likely that we will also be able to locate a nearby area that is hazy and difficult to perceive; it will feel as if it contained too little sensation. The resolution to this condition of imbalance comes about not through an isolated focus on either of the areas of sensation, but rather through a patient moving back and forth between them.

What happens, however, when we locate such a sensation in our head? The possibility for enlarging our focus seems limited to one direction only, to an exploration downward into the area of our neck. The image of the *ourobouros*, however, suggests another possibility. The top of our head and the bottom of our feet are not necessarily separated from each other by the length of the body. From the perspective of our bodily sensation they can be experienced as adjacent to each other! After you have kindled a pronounced awareness of bodily sensation through the *Whole Body* exercise, calmly and patiently focus your attention on your head and feet simultaneously. Without forcing anything to occur, see if you can begin to experience a direct connection between these two most distant parts of the body.

Our ability to experience the proximity of sensation between our head and feet is accompanied by a heightened sense of integration and connectedness. The unwavering hold that the egoic tendency of mind ordinarily has on us spontaneously begins to come undone, as though it has suddenly come face to face with a situation that, while verifiable by perception, has no place within its belief system.

In the face of such a dilemma, all it can do is stand awestruck and dumbfounded. This would be precisely our response if we were to see an amphibious creature maneuver its heavily armored body like a circus contortionist and swallow its own tail. In helping to clarify the nature of tactile geometry, the image of the *ourobouros* is a uniquely appropriate symbol of the experience of integration and flowering that is available to us as we gain awareness of the principles that govern this alternative geometrical perspective.

Exhalation and Pause

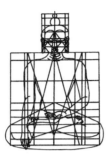

*T*he cycle of breath has four distinct phases: two major ones and two minor ones. In between each inhalation and exhalation, just before the one turns into the other, there is a brief pause. A complete round of breath appears as inhalation-pause-exhalation-pause. Sometimes the pauses between the major phases of the breath are easily noticeable; at other times they are difficult to detect. Ordinarily, if we focus on any one part of this cycle, it is the inhalation. If we become aware that our breathing has become shallow and restricted, we may consciously increase the next inhalation in an attempt to remedy the restriction. Only rarely might it occur to us that a similar effect could be produced by extending the length of the exhalation. Because we are much less aware of exhalation it can be helpful to focus on it. This is especially useful as we attempt to gain familiarity with what it feels like to surrender the weight of the body to gravity.

On each inhalation our torso expands slightly and experiences an upward lift away from the source of gravity. On each exhalation the whole body settles back down in the direction of that source. If the shape of the body exhibits major structural imbalances, and we need to brace ourselves against the force of gravity in order to stand up, it will not be possible for us to exhale fully and completely. In this case the cycle of breath becomes limited and irregular. As the structure of the body shifts to a more balanced configuration, we can allow the weight of the body to drop, especially during a complete exhalation. Now our respiratory cycle can become naturally rhythmic and full. The energetic field of the body can relate to the gravitational field of the earth in a much more harmonious manner. At the height of the inhalation a healthy and dynamic state of tension will be created between these two fields. At the bottom of the exhalation, they may seem almost to merge.

The purpose of this exercise is to uncover your natural rhythm of breath and begin examining what each phase of the breath has to reveal. To begin this exercise it is best to lie down on your back on a soft, supportive surface. Slowly bring your awareness to the process of breath. Watch as the air enters the body, pauses for a moment, and then leaves the body. After a brief pause the cycle begins once more. Try not to manipulate your pattern of breath; simply observe it as it moves in and out. It may be full and smooth or it may be restricted and shallow. It does not matter. Simply observe your breath as it is, without feeling that you need to change it in any way. Are the inhalation and exhalation of equal duration? Is one longer than the other? Can you detect the pauses that separate these two major phases? Often, by bringing awareness to the breath, the pattern of inhalation and exhalation will begin to change spontaneously. If this happens, fine. Allow your body to breathe however it wants. Take your time with this part of the exercise.

After a number of minutes of observation, begin to pay a bit more attention to your exhalation. See how far it extends, and try to determine where exactly it stops. What parts of your body are involved in this phase of the breath? Can you determine where in your body the action of exhalation is centered? For most people the bodily movement that occurs in conjunction with breath does not extend much beyond the area surrounding the major organs of the respiratory system. The play of breath, however, can involve the whole body. This exercise will initiate the possibility of a full-bodied breath, and the next exercise will expand on it.

Continue focusing on the exhalation, but now include an awareness of the gravitational field in your observation of breath. On the next, and each succeeding, exhalation allow the whole body from head to foot to surrender to gravity. Imagine that your body has become a rag doll with no resistance anywhere. Feel the head and neck give in to gravity, along with the shoulders, arms, torso, pelvis, and both legs. The soft surface on which you are lying supports you fully, so there is no need to brace yourself against the pull of gravity. With each exhalation see if you can let go just a little bit more. Use the tactile information that your body is sending you to guide you in your surrender. Scan through your whole body, and see if you can locate any places that are still holding back, resisting giving in to the pull of gravity. Gently let them go on your next exhalation.

If you are aware of gravity, as well as focused on exhalation, you may see that the exhalation is not so much something you have to do or perform as it is something that you can simply allow to occur as part of your surrender to gravity. It happens automatically. As your whole body lets go with each exhalation, the entire cycle of breath may broaden and deepen; it will become increasingly smooth and effortless. Through such a coordinated interaction of breath, body, and an awareness of the pull of gravity you may gain insight into how the whole body — not just the system of respiration proper — can take part in the process of breath. After a few minutes of focusing on the exhalation in this way, you may find your body becoming very relaxed. You may feel as if you are sinking a bit more deeply into yourself or into the soft surface on which you are lying.

The pauses that appear between the major phases of the respiratory cycle are worthy of our attention as well. Ordinarily we overlook them, but as our awareness of breath becomes more acute we can detect their presence much more clearly and come to see how they too play a significant role. In the ancient Tantric tradition of India, the pauses just prior to inhalation or exhalation were seen as doorways through which we might enter into an awareness of divine presence. Inhalation and exhalation are an integral part of our life on earth. In the pauses, it was suggested, we could be afforded momentary glimpses of the realm of the divine. Within this realm alone the source of our being and our true identity could be located.

The pauses are certainly doorways through which we can uncover deeply repressed emotional residue. Ordinarily the pauses are too elusive to detect. They appear and disappear so rapidly that it is difficult to penetrate them or explore what may lie immediately beyond. As we give up the control that we ordinarily superimpose onto our pattern of breath, however, we may find that we experience moments in which the normal pattern of breath momentarily reverses itself and the pauses themselves appear as the dominant phase. During these extended pauses a great deal of repressed emotion may begin to surface. If you observe someone who is experiencing deep grief and sadness, you will notice that the wailing sounds that person may be making and the tears that accompany these sounds occur during an inordinately extended pause following the exhalation. At the other end of the cycle, the frozen expression that we recognize as fear comes during a disproportionately extended pause following an inhalation. The inhalation of breath is what brings a long and extended wail to its completion. In the same way, terror is resolved only when we are able once again to exhale the breath that had become frozen.

Emotional response of any kind coincides with an alteration to the pattern of breath. During the expression of what we consider to be positive emotional states -- love, compassion, contentment, exhilarated joy -- the cycle of breath will become more regular and rhythmic. The opposite is true during the expression of what we call the negative emotions such as fear, sadness, or anger. The breath will become irregular and labored and will be accompanied by some degree of restriction at the top of the inhalation or the bottom of the exhalation.

This latter pattern appears to repeat itself during experiences of emotional release triggered by spontaneous extensions of the pauses between the breath. As you continue to surrender the weight of your body to gravity during exhalation, you may find that your pattern of breath begins to shift significantly. If and when this pattern begins to include extended pauses after either the inhalation or the exhalation, long-repressed emotion may be spontaneously aroused and begin making its way to the surface. As much as you can, yield to the emotion, allowing it to express itself however it wants. Just as you have allowed the breath its freedom of expression, so too can you free the emotion. As the emotions begin to emerge, see how closely tied up they are with a specific pattern of breath. If you allow the emotions to express themselves freely, they will process themselves out. They will gradually subside, and the pattern of breath will shift as well, becoming smoother and fuller once again.

Most of us carry around a repository of unexpressed emotion. There may have been times in our life when it was difficult for us to express and share our sadness, frustrations, fears, or joys. Unable to express these feelings at the moment, we store them in our mind and body. Such repressed emotional residue is like a dark cloud laden with rain. It has the effect of weighing our body down and concealing the brilliant clarity that is to be found at the depths of our being. Whenever we allow a portion of this residue to resolve itself, this innate brilliance shines through once again. We may, if even for a brief moment, get a glimpse of the spark of divinity that lies at our core.

Full-Bodied Breath

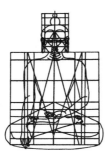

*B*reath and body are profoundly interrelated, and yet most of the time they do not mirror each other as closely as they might. The field of tactility extends from our head to our feet, but the arena of our breath seems confined to a small portion of the body -- the area of our torso surrounding the specific organs of respiration. The major muscle involved in the act of respiration is the diaphragm. Its rhythmic contraction and relaxation causes air to be inhaled and gaseous waste to be expelled. Without its continual pumping action, it is not possible to breathe. The sustained action of the diaphragm causes many of the immediately adjacent muscle groups also to participate in the act of breathing, like ripples that respond to the dropping of a pebble in a pond. This is especially obvious when our breath is strong and full, but can even be detected when our breath becomes shallow and constrained.

This chain reaction of coordinated movement need not be limited to the immediately adjacent area of the lower ribs and belly. It can spread, if allowed, throughout the whole of the body, and in this way the entire body can participate in the action of breath. When this is able to occur, breath and body become as one. No longer separated into different compartments of experience, they can then be perceived as complementary functions, different vantage points from which a single phenomenon can be viewed. Bringing these two ordinarily unaligned aspects of experience back into accord opens the door to a higher realm of experience. This greater awareness is unavailable when the responsive motion of the breath is limited to only a small part of the body.

The purpose of the following exercise is to align breath and body; it will enable you to experience what a full-bodied breath feels like. In order to familiarize yourself with it, you may wish to have a friend slowly read the following pages aloud to you:

Stand for a moment. Feel the weight of your body on your feet. Does your weight appear to fall through the middle of your feet, or do you stand more on the balls of your feet or back on your heels? Is your weight evenly balanced over both your feet, or does most of it appear to rest on one foot or the other? Make a mental note of how it is for you right now in this moment. Now, notice the position of the different parts of your body in relation to one another. Do these different parts appear to flow one into another as interdependent components of an integrated unit, or do they feel disconnected from one another? Do not feel that you need to change anything about the way you are standing. Simply be aware of your body in this posture.

Now lie down on your back on a soft, but supportive, surface. A medium density foam mattress would be ideal. Do not use a pillow for your head; if you're lying on a hard surface, however, you may want to place a pillow under your knees. Rest your hands gently on your belly, one on top of the other. Let your legs be relaxed and comfortably straight, your eyes softly closed. Begin by bringing attention to your breath as it passes in and out of your body. Observe the flow of breath exactly as it is, without feeling that you should adjust its pattern of flow in any way. It may be full and open, with its movements in and out easy to detect and observe. It may be shallow and contained, with its pattern of flow scarcely discernible. Simply accept your pattern of breath exactly as you find it. To observe your breath in this way you should focus on the movement in your torso that accompanies each inhalation and exhalation. No matter how subtle it may be, there is always some bodily movement that occurs during the breath. See if you can determine which parts of your torso respond and which parts stand still. For example, there may be a gentle rise and fall that you can detect in your belly, but very little apparent movement in your chest. There is no need to change anything you find. Continue, passively, to observe your breath in this way for a few minutes.

Now imagine that a friend is standing at your side. On your very next exhalation imagine that they place their hands firmly on your lower front ribs and with a gentle rocking motion, press down to help you expel all the gaseous waste from your lungs. With the help of their firm touch the exhalation is extended as long as possible without causing undue stress. At the bottom of this extended exhalation, they finally release their hands, and a flood of air comes rushing into your lungs on the inhalation that follows. Breathe normally for a few rounds, and notice if your pattern of breath has changed at all. It is possible that it will be fuller and more expansive than it was just prior to this imaginary intervention. After a few normal breaths repeat this process again.

Turn your attention back to your torso. Is it moving in response to the breath in the same way as it was when you first lay down, or has its pattern of movement changed?   When you are able to exhale fully, you create more room for a fuller inhalation to follow. Continue to yield to the breath. Allow it to breathe you in whatever manner it chooses. Inhalations and exhalations follow naturally one upon the other. Responsive bodily movements can be clearly felt and detected. As you continue this exercise, the breath will change constantly. Sometimes it may be shallow and contained; at other times you will be aware of a naturally deep and expansive breath. There are no rules about breathing. Simply let go, and feel your body respond.

Now turn your attention to your hands as they rest one on top of the other on your belly. See if you can begin to allow the residual holding that exists in this part of your body to relax and drop away. Simply let it drop. As you do this, you will be able to detect a subtle, but distinct, movement in your hands in response to the flow of breath. Perhaps they can be felt to move up and down in coordination with the breath, or you may feel one hand sliding slightly back and forth on top of the other. Play with this natural movement for a number of breaths. Once your awareness of it has become quite distinct, forcibly stop the movement, causing your hands to become still and immobile, unresponsive to the flow of breath that has animated them. Notice how unnatural and uncomfortable this feels in comparison. Play back and forth over the course of a number of breaths between holding your hands rigidly and allowing them to respond to the movement of the breath; in this way you can familiarize yourself with the difference in feeling tone that each action creates. Only after having experienced a condition's release do you realize how painful that condition truly was.

Now turn your attention to your elbows. Allow whatever rigidity or holding you feel in your elbows to soften, and see how they too can begin to move ever so slightly in response to the breath. On the inhalation they can be felt to move in one direction; on the exhalation they retrace this movement back to where they started. Also observe how the responsive motion that has been set up in your hands and the movement you are now able to detect in your elbows are directly related to each other. The subtle motion that you feel in your hands initiates a wave-like force that moves up your lower arm and causes your elbows to respond. Once you have familiarized yourself with this connection, hold your elbows and hands very still again, and see what happens in your body. After a few breaths let them go again.

The next place to turn your attention is your shoulders. Once again notice whatever residual holding is to be found in this area of your body, and see how you can allow that holding to begin to soften. Over a number of breaths you will be able to feel that your shoulders too can be felt to move slightly as a natural response to each inhalation and exhalation. A great many factors of influence converge in this part of your body, so it is not possible to predict what this movement will look like. Your shoulders may be felt to rise and fall together in unison, or they may move quite differently from each other. Because the nature of the response that can occur in this part of your body is not subject to easy prediction, it is an excellent area in which to see if you are truly just allowing the movement to occur or if you are somehow participating in the movement and manipulating it in some way. The movement that occurs in a body that is totally responsive to the breath passing through it is natural and effortless. It is not a movement that is self-consciously created or exaggerated. With every breath the pattern of bodily response may change. Just how responsive to this constantly changing flow of respiration can you become?

You have moved your attention through enough parts of your body so that, when you now tighten your shoulders in order to experience the contrast between responsiveness and holding, the difference in feeling may be dramatic. Do this now, and begin to observe what happens. Bringing tension into this one small part of the body sets up a web-like pattern of response, wherein the areas immediately adjacent to your shoulders (and even others that are not so apparently connected) lose their responsiveness as well and become still. Holding in any one part of the body creates holding throughout the entire body. Fortunately, when you release one part of the body, every other part begins to let go as well. You may also become aware of how tightening any part of your body immediately interferes with your ability to breathe. Breath wants to move expansively through the body, much like a wave passing unimpeded through a body of water. Rigidity and holding hamper that potentially expansive movement, limiting it instead to a much shallower and more contained motion. As you again allow your shoulders to let go, see how the pattern of breath immediately changes.

As this wave of softly pulsing movement continues through your body, turn your attention to your neck and head. See how this area too wants to participate in the motion that has been generated in the region of your navel and passes upward through your torso and arms. Like the crest of a wave just before it crashes, this movement naturally wants to extend through to the top of your head with each inhalation. On the exhalation, this pattern of motion appears to retrace itself down your body back again into your navel where, after a brief pause, it begins again.

As your breath has become fuller during the course of this exercise, you may find that your head wants to be positioned differently. Bring your attention to how your head and neck contact the mattress on which you are lying. To find a middle place of balance so that your head is most able to respond to the breath, allow your head to arc up so that your chin points toward the ceiling as the back of your head slides down. Relax your jaw and continue to let it be soft as you slide your head back to a place that is comfortable, but perhaps slightly higher than that to which you've been accustomed. You should now be resting more on the back of your head than on the back of your neck. If you open your eyes for a moment, check to see that you are looking straight up at the ceiling. See how much more space is available in the area of your throat as you breathe with the head positioned in this way. For the sake of contrast, now shift the position of your head so that you are resting more on the back of your neck with your chin tucked in. Notice how the head becomes once again more immobile and unresponsive and how the breath becomes more constricted. Experiment with the placement of your head until you locate the middle position that allows for the greatest comfort and responsiveness. The movement of your head may be obvious or hardly perceptible. Tune in to a sense of expansion with each breath. Feel the head wanting to rise up on the inhalation; then feel it settle on the exhalation. Once you have established this sense of movement, hold your head very still. Become aware of the tightening that occurs throughout your entire body. After a few moments, let your head again relax and begin to respond to the flow of breath. Feel how good it feels to let go in this way.

Just as this wave of motion rises upward from the navel on each inhalation, so too can it be detected to move downward through the lower part of your body. Passing through the pelvis, its presence can even, ever so subtly, be felt to move down into your feet. The whole body, expanding and contracting almost in the manner of an amoeba, can now be felt to participate in the action of the breath. With each inhalation, the whole body expands. With each exhalation, the whole body retracts. There are no deep meanings to seek, no secret significances to uncover; just the feeling of breath moving unimpeded through the body. Remain for some time with your awareness of the whole body as it continues to respond as an interconnected unit to the flow of the breath.

Once you have passed your attention through the whole body in this way, you may want to retrace your path of focus, seeing if any part of your body has unconsciously tightened again, seeing if even greater release and responsiveness may be possible. It may also be helpful to focus randomly on any part of the body, a left knee perhaps or the area around your eyes or jaw. Can you detect any holding in these parts of the body that, in response to the movement of the breath, you can allow to soften? Keep exploring your body in this way.

In this deeply relaxed state you may also be able to observe how the arising of unconscious patterns of thought are invariably accompanied by holding or tightening somewhere in your body; see how this holding also interferes with the flow of breath. Do not try to push the thoughts away when they arise. Rather see if you can locate what part of the body lost its responsiveness as the thought arose. If you are able to pinpoint this bodily location accurately, see that allowing it to regain its responsiveness will cause the thought pattern slowly to evaporate.

There is no set time limit for this exercise. Once you have familiarized yourself with it, just fifteen minute's practice may leave you feeling refreshed and relaxed. At other times, as circumstances allow, it can go on indefinitely. When you feel you have completed the exercise, slowly bring yourself to a standing position. Remember how your body felt before you went to lie down, and see how different it feels now. You may feel more connected to the ground, more balanced over your feet. You may notice that your shoulders and knees are more relaxed, as if the joints have been oiled, and that your head is more effortlessly settled on top of the supporting column of your body. The whole body may be felt to jiggle slightly as the body makes spontaneous adjustments to maintain the ease of balance. See if you can allow your awareness of the body's responsiveness to continue as you walk away.

Heart and Breath

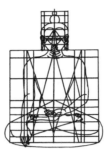

The majority of people living in the West reside in major urban areas. Within these areas are to be found the best and worst of what our cultural bias, in its shaping of the available technologies of our time, has created. The proliferation of sensory objects that these technologies have spawned has been dramatic, and the primary undercurrent of experience that has come to pervade our modern world is one of sensory overload. We are assailed by a constant barrage of increasingly unnatural sights, sounds, fragrances, and tastes whose sheer magnitude leaves us feeling stunned and dizzy. As the orientation of urban life becomes progressively object-oriented, we lose touch with our sense of center and go about our business in a state of numbness. As the variety of sensory objects that confront us daily in the marketplace keeps on multiplying and luring us even further out of ourselves, we demand even stronger sensory stimulation in order to feel anything at all. A vicious cycle is created as the preferred cure for our narcosis only serves to feed the illness.

We speak of being out of touch with our feelings and with the experience of our body. We are aware of how difficult it is to contact and express a wide range of feeling, but we don't know where to turn in hopes of finding the key that might help reestablish that contact and facilitate that expression. Unable to locate the source of real emotion, we satisfy ourselves instead with the fraudulent distortion of emotion that our forms of popular entertainment would have us believe is the genuine article. All that we can become is further confused and disoriented.

True emotion provides undeniable proof of the overlapping of boundaries that we normally think of as separating mind from body. Strong emotion expresses itself simultaneously through the mediums of mind and body, and it does so in a way that makes our conceptual distinctions meaningless. When strong emotion breaks through the protective barrier that is designed to keep its impulse contained, we feel as though it has erupted deep from within the very center of our being. Like a powerful beacon of light, it cuts through the fog of our surface pretense and reveals what is truly happening for us at that particular moment of time.

The epicenters from which different types of strong emotional expression emerge can be traced to different locations in the body. We refer to overwhelming pain and sadness as "gut-wrenching." We speak of outbursts of anger as causing us to "see red." We feel the grip of terror that leaves us momentarily speechless as a suffocating collar around our neck. We label emotions of love, acceptance, and compassionate joy as "heartfelt." They possess a flavor of sincerity that we naturally associate with this most vital of organs.

Our heart is often thought of as our physiological center, the foundation around which all our other organs and systems are oriented and upon which they ultimately depend. It is also regarded, metaphorically, as the center from which wholesome emotional expression pours forth. While anger and sadness erupt fitfully in short bursts of expression which leave us feeling depleted, feelings of love and joy can sustain themselves over a much longer period of time and leave us feeling nourished. Like some inexhaustible mythic spring, we tap the source of these feelings and find that the more we drink from it, the stronger its flow becomes. When we speak of wishing to revive our ability to experience emotion, it is these heartfelt emotions that we are referring to. These are the ones from which we feel estranged; these are the ones for which we long. Within the realm of our heart can be found our most accessible refuge and center, and within the word "heartfelt" can be found the clue that we need to help us find our way back to this center.

Our heart is beating all the time, but except during moments of extreme excitation or exertion, we are hardly ever aware of its presence. It is as though we have a powerful drum, situated just to the left of center in our thoracic cavity, which is being beaten with unwavering consistency throughout the whole of our life. Yet we neither feel it nor hear it! If we can just take a moment and turn our attention to the area surrounding our heart, our mind and body become almost immediately quieter. By listening patiently in the attempt to feel this very vital and prominent beat, we naturally turn inward. Freed momentarily from the sensory overload of the marketplace which draws us so out of ourselves, we are inevitably led closer and closer to the experience of our center. As we continue to focus in this way, we suddenly realize that we can feel the actual thumping of our heart.

So unaware are we of this strong sensation that, when we do finally locate our actual heartbeat, we may experience its presence as jarring or disorienting. Like an unfailing internal metronome, it strikes at us with every beat. Not limited to our heart alone, the effect of each beat can be felt to radiate outward. In the previous exercise we worked to see that our body could be responsive to the movement of our breath. Suddenly we are faced with a whole new self-generating source of movement to which the whole body can subtly respond. If a thought comes to steal away our attention, we realize that our felt awareness of the heartbeat has been removed as well. This is as it should be, for the true center of our being must be a wordless place. The presence of words, therefore, can only lead us outward in the direction of our periphery.

The other major thoracic organ, surrounding and cradling our heart, is our lungs. The rhythmic phases of each of these organs' pulses directly parallel the other's. The phrasing of the heart we refer to as systole and diastole. The phrasing of the lungs we call inhalation and exhalation. If we can add the awareness of breath to our awareness of the beating of the heart, we create a shelter that can offer us a momentary refuge from the assault of sensory stimulation with which the external world bombards us.

This exercise can be particularly helpful if you find that you need a break from this stimulation. If possible, find a comfortable, semi-reclining chair to sit down in or lie down on your back on a sofa or bed. Physical structure and verticality of the body need not be concerns during this exercise. It is only necessary that you are able to relax, to surrender the weight of your body to gravity. Give in to this feeling of settling as much as possible, and gradually start directing your attention toward the middle of your chest where your heart resides. Keep turning your attention inward, focusing patiently on the area of your heart. Without manipulating your experience in any way, simply tell yourself that it is possible to become aware of your heartbeat. The more you keep patiently searching for this vital beat, the freer you become from the captivating hold that the world outside your physical body has on you. Keep on searching, keep on refining your focus, keep on allowing your body to settle until the heartbeat appears.

Once you have located your heart, allow its beat to become loud and prominent. The presence of the heartbeat may become so strong that you may wonder how, ordinarily, you have no awareness of it. Keep on yielding to the strong presence of the beat for some time; there is nothing to fear. Once the heartbeat has established itself prominently and you have spent a few minutes exploring its presence, you can begin to broaden your focus to include the inhalation and exhalation of the breath. See how these two, pulsing forces become intertwined, the major organs of the one cradling the other. Observe the relationship of their rhythms. See how the pulses of one relate to the pulses of the other. Are their rhythms harmonious, or are they out of beat with each other? As you continue to focus in this way, the breath will begin to slow down, and their rhythm may become more synchronous.

The major focus of this exercise is the felt beat of the heart. Surrounding that experience, like an encasing bubble, is the awareness of breath. It is important, as you practice this exercise, to focus on the precise location of the heartbeat. The focus of the breath, however, should be less specific. It is not necessary to fix your attention on any one small part of the body as you broaden your focus to include an awareness of the breath. Simply be aware that you are breathing. After just a few minutes of practicing this exercise, you may find that it is much easier to move out again into the marketplace without feeling so overwhelmed.

Balanced Body, Allowing Body

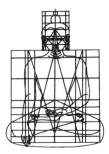

*I*nstead of truly accepting ourselves as we are, most of us choose to manipulate or control our behavior so that our actions will conform to an artificial image we hold of ourselves. The result unfortunately is often the creation of pain and the gradual loss of balance. Unwittingly we get caught in a vicious cycle as physical imbalance begets greater need for control; greater need for control, in turn, disturbs a natural state of balance even more. Learning to give up the need for control depends on our ability to bring the body back again into a condition of balance. By giving up control, we allow tension that has been created in the body, at both physical and emotional levels, to emerge and resolve itself.

The ultimate goal of any form of somatic therapy that seeks to alter the structure of the body is to enable this process of emergence and resolution to begin. Mostly it occurs spontaneously and is not subject to prediction. The pace at which it proceeds may fluctuate dramatically from one moment to the next; so may the nature of the experience that it stimulates. At times exhilarating and comforting, at other times it may be confusing and unsettling, and at other times still it may be quite uneventful. The purpose of this exercise is to initiate this process of somatic unfolding. It is one of the most important skills that we can reacquire.

This most basic of exercises consists of three interdependent phases. The first two set up the conditions for the possibility of the third, and it is through familiarizing yourself with the third phase that you will be able to gain insight into the purpose of the exercise. Each of the phases can be briefly summarized as follows:

1. Bring the body to balance.
2. Surrender the weight of the body to gravity.
3. Allow whatever needs to occur as a result of that surrender.

To begin this exercise take a few moments to assume the most balanced stance available to you. The two most suitable postures for this purpose will be either standing or sitting. In order to become balanced in either of these postures, you need first to bring your awareness in a calm and relaxed way to the experience of your body. Observe the nature of the sensations that are present at this moment. Are the sensations uniform throughout the entire body, or are there a variety of different types of sensations? Can you notice marked differences between the sensations in the right and left sides of the body, between the front and back of the body? Do the sensations in the top and bottom of the body seem to mirror each other, or do they seem unevenly distributed? Take as much time as necessary to compare the relative differences that you perceive.

You don't need to label the sensations or describe the tactile nuances that you observe. Just be aware of them. Rarely will the body appear immediately as a balanced field of uniform sensations. An awareness of the uneven distribution of sensations will allow you to resolve the lack of balance. Keep on exploring the nature of the sensations that exist in your body. As the imbalances become clearer, you will see that they will slowly start shifting on their own. If you can become acutely aware of the experience of your body, your body will begin to bring itself back into a condition of balance. Subtle movements and adjustments may occur from side to side, from front to back. As you keep observing the effect that these shiftings and settlings have on the overall experience of the body, you will come to realize that your body, in the manner of a homing pigeon, has instinctively moved closer to a condition of real balance. The sensations in the body will now be perceived to be more uniform and evenly distributed. It becomes much easier to sit or stand, and this lessening of effort indicates that you are progressing toward balance.

Learning to come to balance in this way is similar to the process by which a child learns to ride a bicycle. While a certain amount of preliminary instruction concerning the mechanics of balance may be helpful, it is primarily a tactile process. A child learns how to ride a bicycle only after he or she, through trial and error, acquires a feel for the experience of balance. It is this feeling that quickly becomes the child's guide. In much the same way, when attempting to refine our experience of balance in the standing or sitting posture, it is the constant feedback of tactile data that lets us know if we are moving closer toward our intended goal. It is helpful to have an understanding of the muscular and skeletal systems of the body and of how a proper relationship between the major parts of these systems contributes to the experience of balance. However, this is not the medium of information that brings us to balance. An over-reliance on this level of knowledge can even keep us from experiencing real balance.

A relaxed body that is symmetrically and compactly arranged around an imaginary vertical axis has a distinct feeling tone associated with it. When the body is lined up properly, this feeling tone will be present. When this feeling tone appears in a body, a person can be said to have found his or her "line." This line is not an anatomical coordinate, but a tactile one. If you look in a mirror and try to position yourself so that the form of your body appears vertical and balanced, you may or may not also encounter the feeling of this line. If you allow the necessary adjustments to your structure to be generated internally, using the sensations of your body as your guide, you will invariably arrive at the experience of this line. Should you look in a mirror at this point, you will be struck by how graceful and balanced the form of your body appears.

Balance is a dynamic condition, not a static one. It is an active, ongoing process more than it is a quiescent state. To ride a bicycle successfully a child must make continual adjustments to propel himself down the road. In the same way, a condition of effortless balance in a standing or sitting posture involves a continual internal dance as our body continues to respond to the wealth of increasingly refined tactile information that keeps presenting itself. True balance comes not through attempting to fortify the structure of the body, but in accepting the fundamentally precarious nature of balance and trusting our body's ability to make whatever adjustments are necessary. Riding a bicycle is not an inherently stable activity. Pedaling down the road, we are always just a hairbreadth away from tumbling over, and yet we rarely do.

Having come to balance, you will now find yourself in a position where you can surrender the weight of your body to gravity without toppling over. Just as you let go of any heavy object that you are carrying, allowing it to drop down onto whatever supporting surface is directly beneath it, so too let go of the weight of your body. Allow it to fall to the earth, to sink down into the ground on which you stand or sit. The weight of your body can actually be felt to give way and trickle slowly downward. As you allow the weight of your body to drop in response to gravity, you will begin to appreciate just how precarious a process effortless balancing is; at the same time you will marvel at how masterly are your body's innate skills in securing that balance.

The third phase of the exercise may now begin in earnest. Through this surrender you may find that a kind of internal drama has begun to unfold as deep layers of unconscious material gradually make their way to the surface of awareness. The form that this material takes may be predominantly tactile, emotional, or mental, or it may appear as any combination of these. Some aspects of this emergent drama may be extremely pleasurable. Others may be quite painful. Your job is simply to accept, as best you can, whatever chooses to emerge without manipulating the play of emergence in any way. It may take some time to familiarize yourself with the organic nature of this process, so be patient as you explore this exercise. If nothing distinct begins happening, turn your attention once again to the first two phases, seeing if you can refine your awareness of balance so that you can more effectively surrender the weight of your body.

As you come into contact with each emergent issue, you will see that it possesses its own motive force. This force will propel it in a certain direction and dictate its pattern of manifestation. There is no need, then, to attempt to force an issue into resolution. Your work is simply to yield to this force. By allowing it to express itself however it chooses, resolution will occur. Your most effective guide during this phase of the exercise is a wholesome trust in the intelligence of your body. If this intelligence is not interfered with, it can resolve whatever internal blockage or issues of conflict might appear and can bring the body back to a condition of balance. One issue may resolve itself only to give rise to a new issue. By allowing the process to continue in whatever direction it chooses to take, you maintain your balance.

Be careful not to place any demands on what you want to occur. While strong responses can and do occur, the process can often be extremely subtle. The most helpful rule of thumb is to expect nothing, but be open to anything.

Each of the phases of this exercise will reinforce, inform, and feed one other. If you are able to accept and work through a particularly difficult sensation or emotion that has presented itself, you will see that your physical structure has become more balanced. With this heightened sense of balance further surrender to gravity becomes possible. With this suddenly refined ability to let the weight of the body drop away, a whole new aspect to your drama may present itself. In this way the exercise keeps propelling itself in the manner of a spiral. The completion of the third phase moves you back again to the first phase, but at an advanced level from where you began.

This exercise is primarily an exercise in allowance. You do not manipulate your body into a position of balance, you allow it to happen. You cannot forcibly rid your body of the experience of weight and heaviness, but you can allow your weight gently to drop away. You cannot force issues to emerge and resolve themselves; you can only accept whatever occurs. Where you can consciously participate is in deciding whether you would prefer to play out the emergent drama in a passive manner or an active one. The passive play, experienced almost entirely internally, expresses itself most effectively through the practice of sitting meditation. The active play, in which the whole body yields to its internal impulses and allows itself to be moved physically through space, is a function of the form of movement described in the Gravity Dance chapter in the first part of this book. Some people will naturally be attracted to one of these forms of expression over the other. Others may choose to experiment with both. In the beginning this exercise may be limited to periods of formal practice. As you become increasingly familiar with its process, however, you may find that it naturally spills over into the play and expression of your movements through life.

Luminous Vision, Luminous World

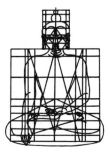

*L*ike a well-tethered anchor that stabilizes a ship at rest and even allows it to ride out turbulent storms without damage, an ongoing awareness of the tactile presence of the body provides a sense of stability and refuge as we open to the world around us. When we expand our focus outward from such a grounded awareness of body, the first and most obvious realm that we encounter is our visual field. Ours remains a predominantly visual culture, and it is primarily through our interpretations of what we see that we come to an understanding of what constitutes reality.

Even though we have become adept at isolating and describing specific objects in our visual field, we rarely see what is in front of our eyes with any real clarity. There are several possible reasons for this. In the first place, it is difficult to have a purely visual experience without labeling, categorizing, and evaluating what we have seen. So instantaneous is this phase in the process of recognition that what we "see" is not so much the object itself as the interpretation that our mind has made about the object. The retina is a completely impartial mechanism. It receives whatever visible light waves the eye is directed toward. Our mind then begins a highly selective process of juggling and evaluating. Translating that data into the names and labels with which it is conversant, our mind focuses only on what seems relevant to its interests and particular philosophical bias. The rest is neatly discarded. Such a process of selection is partial to the extreme.

Just as we concluded that our body is often more a concept than an experience, so too is the world that we perceive through our eyes as much a conceptual field of experience as it is a visual one. We don't just see an abstract play of color. We see a "tree" or a "book." We don't just see a meandering line. We see the number "9" or the letter "K." In appreciating the grace and refinement of Oriental or Arabic calligraphy, it is more helpful not to understand the meaning of what is written. There are drawbacks as well as benefits, however, to our mind's ability to sort out and interpret information. The power of our mind's desire to see what it wants to see enables it to do just that. The mind can distort the data that it is examining so that its desired conclusions and expectations are confirmed. When we fall in love with someone, for example, we will often only be able to "see" our lover's beauty and perfection. Only later will we become more aware of the rougher edges of that person. These are the qualities that our friends, who were perhaps so puzzled by our initial infatuation, were able to see from the beginning.

Relying so heavily on the interpretations of events, we run the risk of isolating ourselves from the sensory reality out of which the interpretations arose in the first place. As we keep on refining our interpretations of the data, there is a danger that our conclusions will not be based on the sensory data itself but on our previous interpretations of that data. This is exactly the danger that Korzybski perceived as he attempted to demonstrate how quickly we remove ourselves from the silent level of bodily experience and enter into the airy realm of abstraction.

Our ability to see things clearly may be further complicated by the disproportionate growth rates of evolution and technology. The motion of evolution proceeds at a veritable snail's pace as compared to the meteoric development of modern technology and the profound proliferation of visual objects that this technology has created. When we move into a culture other than our own, we need a number of days, or even weeks, to assimilate the new sights that so dizzyingly await us; as a species we have not yet been fully able to absorb the dazzling array of visual objects that have appeared on our planet only in the last few hundred years, a period of time which in terms of the spectrum of evolution amounts to nothing more than the merest blink of an eye.

For countless centuries now we have been far more accustomed to viewing the objects of nature than man-made artifacts. In our modern world that balance has been suddenly reversed. A majority of people in the countries of the West live and work in artificial environments in which objects of nature are a rarity or a luxury. The visual cortex of our brain, as well as the surrounding grey matter that functions in conjunction with it, have become taxed to the limit as they attempt to stay abreast of the demands in recognition that our modern world has placed on them. We are forced to work much harder than ever before when we view the modern cityscape, and often our response is to filter out or limit what we actually see; in this way we cushion the abrasive jolt which that cityscape presents us. One of the most effective antidotes to the fatigue that inevitably results from this overstimulation is to go into a wilderness area. Here our eyes can once again feast on scenery that, while perhaps not immediately familiar, nonetheless stimulates a deep response of recognition that leaves us feeling both refreshed and nourished.

True vision is a literally sensual experience that can only occur in conjunction with a deeply sensual appreciation for the tactile experience of the body. Without an awareness of tactility, our visual field appears flat and bland. Our perception of it lacks the vitality, depth, and brilliance of color that it inherently possesses. Our mind, in turn, becomes extremely active. In the manner of the sorcerer's apprentice, the tendency of our mind to interpret, comment on, and evaluate everything that we see can gain so much momentum that it eventually goes out of control. As our thoughts keep multiplying randomly, they themselves become the focal point of our experience; they demand our attention and consume much of our available energy. The original object of attention that stimulated the chain of thought can now be only dimly perceived as though a filter of diffusion has been placed in our line of vision. Accompanying this excursion into the mind is a general tightening of tissue throughout our entire body. Such a condition of holding, be it chronic or only temporary, further interferes with the ability of our senses to function in the manner for which they have been designed.

The purpose of this exercise is to refamiliarize ourselves with the inherent luminosity and three-dimensionality of the visual field. This mode of perception is effectively concealed by the constant interpretative activity of the mind, but it will reappear spontaneously if we can disengage this aspect of mentality and, in effect, silence our mind. It is difficult to see and think at the same time; because we spend so much of our time immersed in our inner monologue, we rarely are able to see things as they are. The key once again, as with so many of the exercises in this section, is to be found in our ability to experience the tactile presence of the body. True clarity of vision, in all its brilliance and depth, comes about only if we are able to see and feel at the same time.

Begin first by bringing awareness to how dull the visual field appears at a moment when the inner monologue of your mind has become particularly active. As the mind chatters on, the visual field looks increasingly flat and featureless. At moments like these your eyes have difficulty focusing on what is directly in front of them. Nor will they be able to adjust their focus easily as the distance between them and what they are looking at changes. This is the condition that people have in mind when they say that someone's eyes appeared to be "glassed over." When you become aware of just how distorted your visual field appears, you may be overwhelmed by a natural urge to bring it back into focus. For a few moments, at least, see if you can forego this urge. Just continue to observe the relationship between the relative clarity of the visual field and the activity of the mind, recognizing that when you become lodged in the mental world of concept, interpretation, and fantasy, your visual acuity is significantly diminished. If you widen your focus to include the tactile field of the body, you may also notice how frozen and immobile your body becomes when you lose yourself in thought.

To bring the visual field into clear and vibrant focus, slowly shift your awareness back into your body, allowing the field of tactility to become palpably present. Be patient and gentle with yourself as you do this. When the chatter of the mind has become particularly active, there will be little awareness of body. Only begrudgingly will the mind relinquish its dominion. Without forcing the mind to shut down or slow the momentum of its chatter, move your attention part by part through the entire body. You will see that the more you become aware of the tactile presence of the body, the more your inner monologue will fade away on its own. The two are mutually exclusive conditions; they cannot be present simultaneously. Continue to shift your attention in this way, becoming ever more aware of the sensations of body. As you become better able to experience the whole of your body as a distinct tactile presence, the appearance of the visual field will become much clearer. Continue to bring as much awareness as possible to the experience of the whole body. As you do this, your eyes naturally soften their gaze, becoming less selective in their focus. Your field of vision automatically broadens.

Ordinarily our vision is highly selective and goal-oriented. Like a hunter in search of his prey, we probe and dissect the visual field, forfeiting any awareness we might have of the wholeness of that field. Instead we content ourselves with a highly fractured vision in which some objects are highlighted while others fade into near invisibility. Like a child rummaging through a pile of toys, we take from the visual field only what we are searching for and ignore the rest. The inherent luminosity and depth of the visual field appear only if we can view that field in its totality, as a whole. For this to happen we must be able to experience the body in its totality, as a unified field of tactile flow.

As you become ever more aware of the experience of your body, shift your visual focus to include as much of the visual field as possible. Without moving your eyes, see if you can determine what the limits of this field are. Where does it end? How far up and down can you see? How far does your vision extend to the left, how far to the right? Continue focusing, as much as possible, on the *whole* of the visual field. As you turn your head or move your eyes, see if you can continue to be softly aware of the entire field. Where previously your eyes might have focused on an isolated object and excluded everything else, see now if your vision can remain inclusive. If an object of interest presents itself, see that it does not have to cause the rest of the visual field to fade away. It will occupy the approximate center of your roughly elliptical visual field, but it is the totality of this elliptical image that has now become your chosen "object" of focus.

Focusing on the whole of the visual field in this way will have a profound effect on the image that appears before your eyes. Colors become extraordinarily rich, their subtle shadings and tonal distinctions clearly apparent. Small details that you ordinarily gloss over can now be clearly perceived. The innate three-dimensionality of the visual field comes into focus. As you continue to enjoy the depth and brilliance of the visual field, even more dramatic awarenesses may reveal themselves to you. You may begin to see how our notions of objects as solid, distinct masses with clearly defined edges distort the reality of those objects' appearance. Quite suddenly, you may be able to perceive that even the most ordinary objects generate a subtle radiance and glow. Objects shimmer at their surface and ever so slightly appear to vibrate. The world comes slowly alive and reveals its luminosity.

There is nothing extraordinary about this mode of perception other than it is not commonplace. We are not trying to superimpose a magical quality onto the field of vision or manipulate it in any way. Our goal is simply to view this field as it is. If we are able to dismantle some of the mechanisms that ordinarily obscure our awareness of the visual field, this is how it, in fact, appears. We can only marvel that this vision is available in its full resplendence all of the time, but that we choose to perceive it only on the rarest of occasions.

The two fields of vision and tactility remain the primary focus throughout this exercise. As our understanding of the relationship between these two fields deepens, we come to see how the reintroduction of discursive thinking (and the attendant loss of tactile presence that accompanies it) causes our perception of the visual field to become once again less vibrant. During other moments, when the relaxed presence of our body allows us to perceive the depth and richness of the visual field in its entirety, we may have our first glimpse of how the sensory fields seem to penetrate one another and become interwoven. At some point the tactile presence of the body may seem to merge with the perception of the visual field, as though one flowed into and out of the other. Our conventional sense of bodily boundary begins to melt away in the face of this awareness. We begin to appreciate the deep sense of connection that underlies the apparently random fabric of the universe.

This exercise can be done anyplace and at anytime. Begin by experimenting privately in places that are familiar to you. Once you have gained some familiarity with the shift in awareness that occurs, you may want to explore the exercise in a more public setting, perhaps as you're sitting in a restaurant or walking down a city street. Over time, the connection between awareness and the experience of body will become very clear.

Penetrating Sound

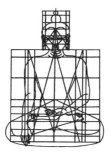

A monk asked Joshu, "What is the Word of the ancients?" Joshu replied, "Listen carefully! Listen carefully!"

I n the same way that we find it difficult to perceive everything that appears before our eyes as a unified visual field, so too are we ordinarily aware of but a fraction of the sounds that are present at any given moment. The issues underlying our diminished awareness of these two sensory fields are essentially the same. As our internal monologue grows in both volume and prominence, our body tightens and contracts. This contraction creates a filter or veil that partially obscures these fields and interferes with the clarity of our perception. The disparity in the rate of growth between evolution and technology is even more of an issue with respect to the field of sound than it is with the field of vision. While the increase in the visual objects that are the product of technology's recent growth spurt can have a sometimes startling effect on us, the new range of sounds to which we now find ourselves so constantly subjected can be horrendously unsettling and disturbing. The soundscape of a modern city can affect the people who live and work there in very distressing ways, leaving them little recourse but to block out what they hear. Studies have been done that suggest that plants grow much better in an environment of pleasant sounds. Certainly the same is true for humans.

The overall effect of this auditory overload has been the numbing of our sense of hearing. Either unwittingly or by design, we manage to mute or filter out much of what appears in the auditory field. Like a worker who forgets to remove the protective earphones that he must wear as a protection against the unsettling levels of noise in his place of work, we muffle the intensity of the field of sound and, as a result, become less aware of its constant presence. Whenever we become less conscious of any aspect of our sensory environment, no matter what the reason, we diminish the awareness of our tactile presence and the ease of balance that accompanies it. The purpose of this exercise is to rekindle our awareness of the field of sound and to acknowledge how this awareness can help us stay grounded within the tactile presence of our body.

The act of perception requires the convergence of three distinct elements: a sensory mechanism, a sensory stimulant, and the consciousness that is aware of the interaction of these first two elements. It is this third element that is ordinarily absent when we become absorbed in the monologue of the mind. Lost in thought, we don't hear much of anything. If we can begin consciously to redirect our awareness to the field of sound, however, the cocoon-like grip of our mind begins to loosen its hold. Gradually, the awareness of body begins to reassert itself. As it does, we can begin simultaneously to experience the range, richness, and depth of the fields of both tactility and sound.

The sequence by which this simultaneous awareness of sensory fields becomes possible is the reverse of the sequence in the previous exercise. In the last exercise we initially brought our awareness to the field of tactility to create a stable base that would enable us to extend our awareness outward and perceive the field of vision clearly and accurately. In this exercise we focus immediately on the field of sound and observe how an accurate perception of this field lessens the volume of our internal monologue, thus increasing our awareness of the field of tactility. The whole of the exercise consists of simply turning our attention to the sea of sounds that surrounds and penetrates us and observing what effect this has on us.

To begin, simply let yourself become aware of the most prominent sound that you can hear at this moment. As you focus on this single source, notice how the sound fluctuates, how it continually changes its appearance from moment to moment. As you keep focusing on the modulation of this most prominent sound, other sounds are bound to appear as well. See how many of these different subsidiary sounds you can recognize. Some of them may be very distinct and recognizable; others may appear as nothing more than the faintest of hums. See if you can detect the sound that exists the furthest distance away from you. See also if you can detect the sound that is closest to you. As you keep taking inventory of all the individual sounds that are present, see if your focus can broaden so that you can maintain a simultaneous awareness of all of them. From moment to moment, the soundscape constantly changes. Are you able to stay within the experience of the present moment, keeping abreast of these changes, or does your mind tend to linger on the interpretation of a sound long after it has disappeared? When a new sound appears, are you able to mark its entrance clearly and precisely, or does it take some time before you realize that it has appeared? Paying attention in this way to the overall field of sound is not unlike the process that occurs when you listen to a symphony orchestra. A multitude of different sounds can be heard at once, becoming alternately louder and softer in relation to one another; they deftly weave their way as individual threads through the overall pattern of the piece of music. Some are naturally more prominent than others, and yet the enjoyment to be gained from listening to the performance depends on your ability to remain aware of the voices of all the instruments. During this exercise, as much as possible, see if you can remain focused on the overall pattern of the field of sound rather than becoming exclusively sidetracked by any one thread that may appear.

Some sounds are so loud that they obscure any other sound that might be present. In a comfortable suburban environment we may, at any given moment, be able to identify as many as a dozen or more sounds, but in an industrial environment the sound of one large machine in operation may be all that we can hear. The internal monologue of the mind can function like an element of sound that, much like the machine, can so dominate our auditory awareness that we hear little else. Unlike the machine, however, it is a counterfeit sound, its source and medium of expression being much more conceptual than truly auditory. While it often seems as though we faintly "hear" it, as if a voice similar to our own were speaking to us from a distance, its sound is hollow and unreal. It only relates to the world of real sound by obscuring our awareness of that world, functioning much like static that interferes with the transmission of radio signals into our home. As we continue to shift our customary focus, observing the play of true sound, the internal monologue gradually recedes until a moment is reached when it becomes silenced. At these moments we are able to observe that each distinct sound has an almost sculptural quality to it. While the "sound" of our mind is flat and dull, real sound can be perceived as almost three-dimensional in its auditory presence. The appearance of this full and rich awareness of sound is inevitably accompanied by a silencing of the mind and by a reappearance of an awareness of tactility. Just as with vision, we cannot hear and think at the same time. We can only hear and feel.

Mostly we think of sounds as being external to ourselves. However, if we find ourselves in a very quiet setting, we will find that many of the sounds we can hear and identify come from inside our body. This becomes especially apparent if we move into the recesses of a deep cavern or walk across a still desert valley. Our breath, the beating of our heart, and the high-pitched frequency of our nervous system are always with us. Only death silences them. Just as a loud machine makes it difficult to hear what someone is saying to us, so does our normal auditory environment obscure our awareness of these subtle internal sounds. As we become increasingly sensitive to these sounds, however, we can begin to appreciate the richly complex musicality that is contained even within the presence of silence. Sound is everywhere. It penetrates us whether we welcome it or not.

Afloat in this sea of sound, the hard line of separation that we ordinarily draw between our inner and outer worlds becomes significantly less delineated. Sounds emanate from inside our body; others come from a source outside of our body. Both, however, are inseparably interwoven into the overall fabric of the field of sound. We can usually identify the source or direction from which a specific sound appears to emanate. However, to distinguish internal and external sounds as belonging to decidedly different categories of auditory experience is misleading; it would be like insisting that sounds we can hear off to the right side of our body are qualitatively different from ones we can detect off to our left. Like a powerful fragrance that moves through solid walls, the field of sound is able to surround, emerge from, and even pass right through the apparent physical frame of the body.

Attending to sound in this way, we gain rapid insight into both the truth of change and the experience of present time. Unlike visual objects which give the impression of immutability and continuity, whose form may appear unchanged over time, sounds can only be perceived as elements in flux, constantly changing their appearance from one moment to the next. Their evanescent nature is immediately apparent. Even the most stable of sounds can scarcely last for more than the briefest moment before some trace of alteration can be detected. Until we cleanse our perception and are able to see the shimmering glow that visual objects emit, the field of vision cannot nearly reveal the truth of constant change as easily as can the field of sound. As we keep attending to the passage of sound, we become automatically grounded within the experience of present time. We may look at a visual object, turn our head away, and then look back with the reasonable expectation that the visual object will still be there in a form fundamentally similar to that of just a moment ago. Once a sound is gone, it is gone forever. The same, of course, is technically true of visual objects as well. The stream is constantly changing whether it appears to be or not. Attending to the field of sound, however, it is impossible to fool ourselves into believing otherwise.

Large Body: The Mandala of Reality

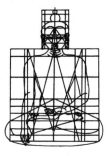

*J*ust as our individual limbs are capable of performing actions quite independently of one another, but are nonetheless interdependent parts of the same body, so too can our sensory fields, with their distinctly different mediums through which information is conveyed, be perceived as interdependent limbs of a larger body of experience. All of the previous exercises have focused on a specific part or aspect of this larger body: the fields of vision, of sound, and of tactility and its relationship to mentality. Having familiarized ourselves with these isolated sensory fields, we are now in a position to start putting them back together into one coherent piece. Our work here is similar to that of an astronomer who begins his observation of a distant galaxy by focusing first on individual stars. Once he has familiarized himself with the uniqueness of their properties, however, his next task is to see how, in spite of their apparent differences, they all fit and flow compatibly within the larger system of the galaxy.

The whole of our experience is composed of six different sensory fields: vision, sound, tactility, mentality, taste, and smell. Of these six the first four are primary. The latter two generally play much smaller roles in the overall composition.[13] For this reason it is not so easy to isolate them in as meaningful a way as we have done in the last two exercises with vision and sound. In the same way that we have learned to experience our physical body as a unified field of tactile flow, so too can we learn to experience these six fields as structural components of a highly cohesive and unified larger field.

---

13) Different sensory fields are dominant during different periods of history; indeed, the progression of history itself can be traced to the fluctuation that has occurred in the relative strengths of these sensory fields. Our sense of vision, for example, is currently our predominant sense, even though our technology has shifted in a way that is undermining the primacy of the visual field. Ten thousand years ago, in what Julian Jaynes (*The Origins of Consciousness in the Breakdown of the Bi-cameral Mind*) terms "pre-conscious man," the auditory and tactile fields were far more

Most of the time the information that is presented in these various fields is used to support our concept of the unbridgeable separation that underlies the structure of reality. The fields are seen as separate mediums of expression, each in turn portraying an image of the world as a compilation of isolated objects and events. Within this bifurcated vision the fabric of reality is irrevocably cut into at least two pieces. Each and every object and event is seen as an island unto itself, bearing only the most superficial expression of linkage with all the other objects and events in its immediate proximity. From the perspective of linguistics, a subject must remain eternally separated from the object that completes its act. On a human level such isolation becomes a breeding ground for fear, loneliness, and distrust, and for the condition of suffering that inevitably follows. The purpose of this exercise is to see that we can take this same information and, without manipulating it in any way, arrive at a wholly different conclusion and understanding about the composition of reality. If our six fields of experience can come together compatibly into a unified pattern of sensorial flow, then the feeling tone that will be generated is one of deep connection, relatedness, and wholeness. Such a possibility has traditionally found its most explicit graphic expression in the image of the mandala.

Mandala is the Sanskrit word for circle — a straight line that curves on itself until its ends eventually join together and are separate no more. It is a transcultural image, appearing spontaneously again and again at different times and in different places whenever humans have been moved to give graphic description to their feelings of, or yearnings for, wholeness, balance, and flowering. The image can take shape in an infinite variety of ways, and some mandalas become extraordinarily complex and detailed. Underlying this surface complexity, however, two basic structural elements can be detected. The overall form of a mandala will always appear as a markedly symmetrical pattern radiating out from a central point of reference:

Figure 9.

dominant, the field of mentality significantly less so. Wilhelm Reich's equation of the body with the unconscious is a relative truth for our era, a reflection of the fact that at this point in our history, mankind has managed to lose touch with the experience of the body as perceived through the field of tactility. At other periods in history, when our mode of awareness shifts and we become less conscious of a different sensory field, that equation would have to be altered. Naming vision, sound, tactility, and mentality as the four primary fields for this exercise will be valid for most, but perhaps not all, people. There are, for example, people for whom the sense of smell is still very prominent. (The olfactory sense has more associative endings into the brain than any of the other senses.) As a final note it could be mentioned that human beings appear to be the only species that has the ability to alter the sensory field that is the most dominant for them. This ability has played a significant and reciprocating role in our relatively rapid evolution. As we evolve, we create new technologies that alternately encourage or discourage the dominance of different sensory fields; this shifting of the ratio of sensory dominances then forces us to shift and evolve some more.

Drawn as an image on a flat surface, many mandalas are oriented, much like a navigational compass, toward the four cardinal directions. When mandalas take sculptural form in three dimensions, as they do in Buddhist *stupas* and Hindu temples and shrines, there are two more directional coordinates that must be taken into consideration. In addition to the conventional orientations of North, South, East, and West, there is also the zenith and the nadir: the sky above and the earth below. The human body is a three-dimensional structure with six major anatomical planes of reference. There are also six major sensory fields which, when combined, form the whole of experience, the complete perceived image of the universe that is available to us at any given moment in time. Might it be possible to construct a three-dimensional mandalic image using the human body as our point of orientation and assigning each of the six sensory fields to one of the six directional coordinates?

The center of a two-dimensional mandala is a point. Moving outward into the next dimension, the center of a three-dimensional mandala will be a vertical line. When standing erect, the human body can be seen to be oriented around just such a vertical line. The ability to experience the effortlessness of balance through "finding one's line" is central to experiencing the deep connection and integration of parts that the mandalic image we are constructing here is attempting to convey. Within our mandala, then, it is easy to equate the human body itself with the center point of the image. This is an appropriate assignation, as all of the sensory fields are functions of human experience. All appear to emanate from and relate back to the reference point of the human body.

Most of the time the field of mentality is narrowly equated with the process of thought. It is, of course, much more than that, but for our purposes here this most conventional aspect of mentality is sufficient to give us a clue as to where it should be located within the mandala that we are creating. People often equate being lost in thought with being lost in their heads, and certainly the most superficial patterns of thought do appear to be situated there. Our head is located at the uppermost region of our body; we can assign the field of mentality to the direction of the zenith, the point in the sky directly overhead.

When viewed as a whole, a mandala conveys an image of perfect balance. Within a condition of balance any estrangement is capable of being reconciled and any apparent contradictions canceled out. We may observe any one of its quadrants separately and see that what is represented there appears to be the exact contradiction to what is depicted in the quadrant directly opposite it. The overall image of the mandala, however, suggests to us that these apparently opposing forces or representations are not necessarily as contradictory as we ordinarily believe them to be. Mind and body are often conceived as contradictory and separate aspects of experience. If this conception takes firm root within our system of belief, we may create a significant psychic fracture that affects every aspect of our lives. This split will often manifest as the feeling that the head and the rest of the body are disconnected from each other, that the priorities of mind and body are in conflict. The nadir, the point beneath our feet, is located directly opposite the zenith, and it is to this direction that we can assign the field of tactility. The body is formed from the elements of the earth, and when it dies it will decay back into those elements. It is, furthermore, primarily through our sense of tactility that we are able to perceive the true nature of bodily experience and of the relationship that exists between it and the gravitational field of the earth. When this experience reveals itself fully, we speak of feeling "grounded."

Our eyes can only see what is directly in front of them. Our sense of hearing on the other hand is one of the most effective tools we have to ascertain what is going on in back of us. A person who is thought of as having "eyes in the back of his head" is someone who has a particularly acute sense of hearing. With this in mind, we can assign the field of vision to the direction in front of our body and the field of sound to the direction behind us.

This leaves only taste and smell and the directions to our right and left. Certainly taste and smell are related to each other so that it is appropriate that they should be directionally linked. When we eat our food, for example, both of these senses function in combination with each other. Beyond this, however, there are few obvious clues to help us determine to which remaining coordinate they should be properly assigned. With these two fields, our assignation may appear somewhat more arbitrary. The left side of the body, under the influence of the right hemisphere of the brain, has traditionally been associated with the more receptive, intuitive, feminine aspects of human experience and expression. The right side of the body, itself under the influence of the left hemisphere of the brain, is seen to represent the more initiating, logical, masculine aspects. Stereotypically, woman is seen as much more sensitive to, and interested in, the world of smell. Hers is the sex that is portrayed as appreciative of the subtle shadings of different fragrances of flowers and perfumes. The masculine mentality is stereotypically portrayed as being too gross and impatient to appreciate such subtlety. His "tastes" tend more to the strong and obvious. Men have traditionally indulged more in food and drink than have women. For the purposes of our diagram let us assign smell to the direction to the left of the body and taste to the direction to the right. The image that we have constructed now looks something like this:

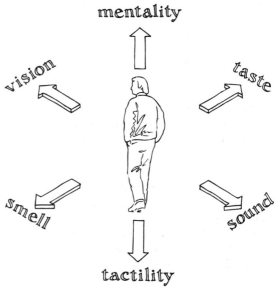

Figure 10.

A mandala is an image of wholeness, a pictorial or sculptural representation of the experience of unification and relatedness. Much like a road map of the psyche, it can help point us in the direction of our goal and inspire within us confidence that the journey is a feasible one to embark upon in the first place. While the purely aesthetic element in any object of art is an important factor in determining how effectively that object is able to convey its intended message, the ultimate value of a mandala is not to be found in its appearance alone. Its true importance lies in what we can learn from it and in what it ultimately suggests.

The first thing of value that we can learn from this image is that the center in man is not a point, but a line. We speak at great length of becoming centered or of finding our center, and in the process we search through the framework of our physical body to determine where this centermost point might be located. Some people say that our center is to be found deep within the experience of the heart. Others view the pelvis as the generative source or center out of which all energetic expression emerges. In one of the Japanese Buddhist traditions the true center in man is equated with the *hara*, a specific point situated within the abdomen, just a few finger's width below the navel. Great thinkers might argue that their head is the center of their being. If we become aware of the importance of maintaining a grounded connection with the earth, we could just as convincingly argue that our feet and lower legs are our true center.

The problem with all these assignations is that they conceive of man's center as a point rather than a line. While most animals have a single, pointed characteristic that accurately describes their most prominent function or pattern of behavior, the challenge facing every human being is in becoming truly multidimensional. There are times in our lives when all of the above-mentioned expressions are appropriate, and so the true mark of a centered individual may more accurately be perceived as his or her ability to be flexible, to respond to the demands of a situation in as relevant a manner as possible. Some situations allow us to indulge in reveries; others demand that we be able to think and reason with calculated precision. Certain events summon forth an impassioned emotional response; others require that we detach ourselves from the event, maintaining a calm and unperturbed bearing.

While different parts of the body may be correctly seen as the source of specific human functions and expressions, none of them enjoys an exclusive position of primacy over the others. What these expressions (and the bodily locations that are associated with them) all have in common is that they are individual points along a common line. The ability to come to balance, to "find one's line," allows us to move easily up and down the spectrum of human expression however the situation in which we find ourselves requires. Ida Rolf would often say that only a body that is balanced around this imaginary central axis is capable of moving and responding freely in any direction whatsoever. To find one's line is to find one's center.[14] Becoming overly focused or fixated on any one point along that line limits our potential range of expression.

---

14) The only drawback to the three-dimensional mandalic image that we have drawn here is that it is static. When the body begins to move through space and time, we should more accurately include a fourth dimension. This dimensional increment will transform the centermost image of the

The most important message that a mandala can convey is that the seemingly disparate elements that are portrayed in each of its sectors are all parts of a greater, cohesive whole. Focusing as we ordinarily do on the periphery of a mandala, we are faced with a multitude of sensory mediums that appear to have little in common. The many different objects that we can perceive in these many different fields are taken as evidence of the inherent discontinuity and splintering of reality. However, if we can shift our customary focus and broaden it to include the whole of the mandalic image, an altogether different vision of reality presents itself. If all of these seemingly different fields can be experienced as merging with and interpenetrating one another -- coming together as a unified, larger field -- then our notions of disjointedness and separation have to be discarded as inaccurate. It is precisely the possibilities of this alternative way of viewing reality that the mandala suggests.

The key to such a shift in perspective can be found in the recognition that all the peripheral elements in a mandala appear to emanate from the single, common source pictured at its center. The centermost point of this mandala is the human body. Here and only here can be found the hub capable of unifying the different elements that appear to emerge and radiate out from it. We can attempt to isolate these different fields and to study them independently of one another. Such an approach, however, only serves to take us further and further away from actual experience. At any given moment all of these fields, in differing ratios and proportions, are present. Any attempt to isolate one of these fields, to view it out of the greater sensory context of which it is a part, can only diminish our awareness of the reality we are supposedly attempting to study and observe. As has been stated so often in this book, body is not a concept but an enormously rich, multi-dimensional experience. As we move our attention back toward the center of the mandala, back toward the body, we have no choice but to let our concepts of reality fall away and embrace instead the richness of immediate experience.

Where do the perceptions of all these different sensory fields exist if not within the body itself? This realization is the central message of the mandala. The movement between the center and periphery of the mandala is in two directions. Moving out from the center, we must include the elements of the periphery, which are then recognized never to have been independent of the center in the first place! The ability to perceive the sensory fields, then, is not only a function of the human body; the perceptions of these sensory fields *are* the actual body itself. The center and periphery are contained one within the other. They are, in fact, identical.

While ordinarily we *conceive* of our body as this familiar shape and form, we are now asked to *experience* our body as the sum total of our individual sensory

---

mandala just as our movement from a two-dimensional image to a three-dimensional image changed the center from a point to a line. It is Judith Aston's elegant observation that the line, when taken into movement, becomes a nonspecific spiral. The image of spiraling is able to convey the spatial patterns and movements of a balanced and highly resilient body in a much richer and more accurately descriptive manner than can the lesser dimensional image of a line. Each of these images can be seen to build upon the one preceding it. To find our center, we need first to find our line. Spiraling, then, is our line taken into movement.

perceptions. The whole of the visual field, not just our physical shape and form, is the visible aspect of our experiential body. All the sounds, thoughts, sensations, tastes, and smells that we experience at any given moment are also contained therein. The form of such a "body" is extraordinarily ephemeral, changing its appearance constantly from one moment of perception to the next. At one moment one field predominates, at the next moment another, and all the time the contents of the individual fields are appearing and disappearing with extraordinary rapidity.

How can this vision be effectively put into practice? How is it possible to make this mandala the basis of our actual experience? The easiest way is to take constant inventory of the sensory fields, acknowledging their continual presence and watching how their contents and relative strengths shift and turn. This does not mean that we have to manipulate our awareness of these different fields in an attempt to balance them out equally, but only that we remain vigilant in our observation of the relative presence of these fields. At different moments, some will naturally be more prominent than others, and much of the time smell and taste may be so neutral as to appear absent. However, the four major fields, in constantly varying proportions, are always present during our waking hours. During those moments when we become engrossed in any one of these fields to the exclusion of the others, we lose the balance of the mandala and the experience of union that it represents. At those moments it becomes necessary once again to take patient inventory and to include anew the presence of at least the other three major fields within the broad spectrum of our field of awareness.

You might, perhaps, begin this inventory by acknowledging what exists in your visual field at the present moment. Without focusing on a specific object in that field, see if you can simply soften, and then broaden, your gaze to include an awareness of the field as a whole. Pay as much attention to the periphery of the visual field as you ordinarily pay to what appears in its center. As you continue to do this, you will see that your awareness of the field of tactility will become heightened as well; only when you can experience your body as a unified field of tactility can you also maintain a passive, awareness of the whole of the visual field. At some point, as your simultaneous awareness of these two fields intensifies, you will see that a curious merging begins to occur, as though the field of tactility (which we ordinarily assume to be limited to the framework of our physical body proper) begins to radiate outward, to permeate and ultimately coalesce with the visual field. Such an experience of merging is only available if you can maintain a heightened state of relaxation and balance in the body. As soon as your body tightens in any manner of reaction, the two fields will again separate.

Now add the field of sound to your awareness. Simply accept whatever sounds your ears can detect at the present moment and include these changing auditory patterns as an element in the overall, unified sensory awareness that you are constructing. Visual objects are present. Sensations are present. Sounds are present. See how the fields begin to intermingle. As they come together and align themselves with one another, they can be felt to occupy the same experiential "space." See how adding yet another sensory field to your awareness necessitates even greater relaxation and balance in order not to lose the feeling of merging that automatically begins to occur.

As you maintain awareness of the interpenetration of these sensory fields, watch to see if any thoughts or emotions begin to surface. If they do, simply include them as best you can within the broad format of your overall, inclusive awareness. If thoughts become too turbulent or dominant, the experience of merging will become gradually less distinct. See if you can detect that the veil of thought has been accompanied by tightening in one part of the body or another. Often by gently letting go of the tension that has accumulated at a physical level, the field of mentality clears, and the experience of merging once again appears in all its richness and depth. When the body is relaxed and the awareness of vision, sound, and sensation is keen, it may appear that the field of mentality disappears completely. In such a silent, undisturbed state, however, awareness itself is always present. The ability to remain clear and focused can in time be perceived as an aspect of the field of mentality that is every bit as recognizable as the more familiar expressions of thought and emotion.

Your vision of the interpenetration of these primary fields may be clear and precise one moment, hazy and indistinct the next. As it fades, simply start over. Begin again by asking yourself what is real *at this very moment* in your visual field. What is real at the level of physical sensations? What sounds are present *right now*? What thoughts? Keep doing this over and over again, making sure that you don't overlook even the smallest aspect of an individual field, until your experience of the vision once again materializes. If the fields of taste and smell are presenting themselves strongly, include them as well.

In many ways this exercise is a direct reflection of the very first exercise in this section. In both of the exercises you are directed to move your attention over and over again through each and every part of the body. The difference between the two exercises lies in what constitutes the components of body. In the first exercise it was the conventional limbs and tissues of the physical body. In this exercise it is the ever-shifting perception of the six sensory fields of experience. Once you have familiarized yourself with each separate part of this larger body, you can begin to broaden your focus just as you did in the first exercise. Now begin to experience the whole of this larger body as a unified, multi-sensory field. As you remain comfortably open to an awareness of this larger, inclusive field, a significant ontological shift may begin to occur. Your sense of identity, your understanding of the distinction between inner and outer, and your understanding of distinction and separation itself will all be gradually transformed. These notions will be perceived to be only relatively true at best, distortions of a deeper, more inclusive level of embodied experience to which we all have access. At this level the experience of the mandala is made real. You become the ever-changing play of sensory patterns that continually imprint themselves, for the briefest moment, on your screen of awareness. This play itself becomes your body.

In the face of such an overwhelming transformation, what then becomes of the actual physical body that is so dear and familiar to us? Formerly, its perimeters defined the limits of our identity, the limits of our uniquely personal world. Now it is simply the center or reference point, a virtually nonphysical coordinate, through which our experience of these six sensory fields, the many tissues and limbs of our large body, can be funneled. If anything, this makes the actual physical body all the more precious, for unless it is functioning at its physiological and psychological best there is little possibility of our experiencing ourselves in this new way. In many spiritual traditions the body is referred to as our temple, and we are cautioned to treat it accordingly. Even more precisely, the body can be identified with the centermost shrine of a temple, that place which houses the most venerated objects of faith and where the most sacred visions can be revealed.

Our comprehension and experience of this large body of perceptual reality reveals to us a sacred vision of the world in which we live. If we apply ourselves to bring this vision into clear and vibrant focus, our understanding of ourselves and our world becomes radically altered. The disconnection and unrelatedness that so dominate our ordinary conception of the world have no choice but to fall away in the face of the deep merging and interpenetration that we begin to experience. This merging occurs as all the sensory fields, contrary to our conventional understanding, are perceived to coalesce in the same, identical location, the locus of experience. At this locus there is separation no more, but only union.

The Locus of Experience

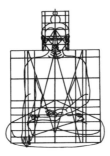

Many people enjoy seeing an occasional movie as a form of entertainment. We value movies for their ability to move us to laughter or tears, to dazzle us with images both real and imaginary, and to broaden our understanding of the planet on which we live. We also use movies as a way of removing ourselves, however momentarily, from the subtle sense of discontent that pervades our lives. We become so engrossed in the images passing before us on the screen and so involved with the characters being portrayed that we tend to lose all sense of ourselves. More precisely, we lose touch with the field of tactility and remove ourselves, for the duration of the film, from an awareness of our body. At these times, our sense of center shifts from a place inside our body out onto the passing images projected on the screen.

It is not inappropriate to look upon the watching of a film as a metaphor for the way in which we live our lives. Often we become so captivated by the events transpiring around us that we limit our awareness of how these events affect us. We perceive an object or event as existing outside ourselves and, in so doing, lose sight of the fact that objects and events "exist" for us only insofar as the sensory and cognitive mechanisms of the body can perceive and know them. When an event in our life has this kind of impact on us, we speak of being "taken out" by it. In the boxing ring, from where this expression derives, a powerful blow can "take out" an opponent and render him temporarily unconscious. If our attention becomes so drawn to an event or occurrence that we forget about the experience of our body, we too become less conscious. On a more subtle, internal level, we experience this same kind of disorientation whenever we attach ourselves to the images, thoughts, and fantasies that make up the inner monologue of our minds. During those moments when we become identified with the contents of our mind, we effectively relinquish the awareness of our body. Our behavior and experience of self become limited. As we become more aware of the nature of the passing show that is taking place both inside and outside of our body, we come to realize how similar in form it is to the movie we see projected on the screen in a theatre.

The first part of this exercise involves focusing your attention primarily on the experience of your body the next time you go to see a movie. In a sense, there are two "movies," two main objects of interest, that vie for your attention whenever you sit down in a theatre. One is to be found in the constantly changing images and sounds of the movie that appears on the screen. The other is to be found within your own body. The conventional movie is visual and auditory; the other is primarily tactile. Ordinarily, the first of these movies receives our primary attention while the other receives only token attention at best. During this exercise, see if you can reverse the relative importance of these two "movies." As you sit comfortably in your theatre seat, allow your breath to remain natural and relaxed and the experience of your body to take up the foreground of your attention. Grounded in this way within the tactile presence of your body, you will see that you are not so readily taken out by the images on the screen, but are able instead to remain within yourself.

An important key to maintaining contact with the experience of your body is the constant awareness of breath. It is quite easy to merge an awareness of the tactile presence of the body with a carefully focused awareness of the movement of the breath. The two are so interrelated that the one naturally follows the other just as a shadow follows an object exposed to a strong source of light. Unlike many Buddhist exercises that are designed to enhance concentration by focusing on how breath affects a small, isolated part of the body, in this exercise allow your focus to be relaxed and nonspecific. It is sufficient to simply be aware, in the most passive way, that you are breathing. Such a nonspecific focus will permit you to maintain a simultaneous awareness of the passage of the breath and the whole of the body. It will also evoke a feeling tone of relaxation. This feeling tone will proceed undisturbed as long as you are able to maintain your primary focus on breath and body.

In this relaxed and grounded state, the images on the screen can seem to wash over you and pass away in much the same way that an ocean swell washes over, but is not able to budge, a large and secure boulder situated just at the shoreline of a beach. As soon as you lose your primary focus, as soon as you get caught up in the images on the screen or the dialogue of the soundtrack, the awareness of body quickly fades, and your breath will become shallower and lose its rhythmic flow. If you become aware that you have been unwittingly taken out in this way, simply start again. Return your focus to your breath and the tactile field of your body. See how long it takes you to become securely grounded within this dual awareness. Allow the images on the screen once again to come to you.

In the second part of this exercise, we take what we have learned in the theater and apply it to the motions of our lives. The images on a movie screen look continuous, and yet we know that they are but the compilation of thousands of individual frames projected so rapidly that they give the illusion of continuity. The world we live in also appears continuous and substantive, but as our understanding and experience of *anicca* deepens, we realize that this is not so. Everything that we can experience is changing from moment to moment; the forms with which we are so familiar, composed as they are of subatomic particles and rapidly oscillating wavelets of energy, are undergoing a constant process of appearance and dissolution. What we call reality, then, this compilation of objects and events that appear in our six sensory fields, is but a kind of movie projected onto the screen of our awareness. We are ordinarily so immersed in it, however, that it becomes exceedingly difficult to view with the same kind of perspective, distance, and objectivity with which we learned to view the more conventional movie in the first part of this exercise.

Whereas in a theater we are but an observer watching a movie that is being projected out onto a screen, we now find that we are simultaneously all of these: observer, movie, projector, and screen all in one. Certainly I am the principal and most interested observer of the unfolding drama that is my life. Viewing this drama as a kind of movie, however, I see that it is also nothing but myself, composed as it is out of my perceptions of the six sensory fields of experience. Moreover, it must be acknowledged that my role in this increasingly complex process is anything but passive. Only through my active participation can I experience the objects in these sensory fields. Accordingly, I have just as important a role in projecting these objects as have the objects themselves. Finally, I can only conclude that the projector and the screen are identical; the images appear on the very same screen of awareness that was involved in projecting them in the first place!

In the face of such a bewildering array of apparent contradictions, how can we maintain the same kind of composure and balance which, in the first part of the exercise, enabled us to remain comfortably relaxed within ourselves and not be drawn out by the images on the screen? The technique of fusing our awareness of breath and body will once again be of help, but in a more limited way. The problem is that now we are required to recognize the field of tactility itself, which formerly provided us with so much stability, as yet another of the shifting components in the movie that we are observing.

What will be even more helpful and stabilizing will be to remind ourselves constantly of our location in space. Sitting comfortably in a movie theatre, we can easily determine this spatial location with exactness and certainty. We are seated on our chair, and indeed much of the focus of the exercise was an attempt to keep our awareness centered on the experience that was sitting in the chair. In the first part of this exercise our location in space was, for all purposes, constant and unvarying.

In observing our movements through life, can we uncover a similar kind of location capable of providing as fixed a perspective from which to view the passing show? Certainly this location cannot be a conventionally spatial one like a specific chair in a movie theatre. Unlike our experience in the theatre, we are constantly moving from one place to another with only temporary stopovers along the way. If, however, we can conceive of an experiential rather than a three-dimensional location, then we can find just such a coordinate, and that is the locus of experience itself. Whether I am sitting quietly in a meditative state or running rapidly along a mountain path, the location in which I am experiencing what is happening to me is, in both cases, identical. Indeed, it is the only place where I can experience anything at all. As a vantage point from which to observe the unfolding drama of my life, it is just as fixed and unvarying a location as is the seat in the theater on which I sit to watch a film.

This somewhat mysterious spatial coordinate is nothing other than the centermost point of the mandala that we constructed in the previous exercise. While we equated that point with the human body, we also suggested that the human body is nothing but *experience*. With this kind of approach and understanding, we can see that the center of the mandala, what we conventionally call human body, is the "location" wherein all of the information that appears in the different sensory fields is actually experienced. When working with the mandala in the previous exercise, we focused on remaining continually mindful of the changing contents of the six sensory fields that appear in the peripheral sectors of the image. The purpose of this current exercise is to see that we must also include an awareness of the centermost point as well. Remaining mindful of this experiential coordinate, we complete the mandala. When taking inventory of our present experience, we must not only keep on examining what is real right now in the fields of vision, sound, tactility, mentality, taste, and smell. We must also include an awareness of where it is that we are experiencing these fields. In this way the center and periphery of the mandala are experienced to be one and the same. The feeling tone that accompanies such a realization is one of great stability and certainty.

The next time you are walking down a street, see if you can recall what it felt like the last time you were in a movie theater sitting calmly and securely, the experience of your breath and body merged, the images on the screen coming to you rather than drawing you out to them. All around you a movie of another sort is taking place. It too will challenge you to find a place of refuge from which you can safely view the passing show. If you discover this place of stability, you can remain unaffected by the often turbulent flow of images that project themselves so luringly onto the screen of awareness. All around and within you, there is movement and change. As you move slowly down the street, see if you can contact this place of refuge that does not appear to move.

Sacred Space

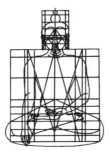

Viewed in sequence, the exercises that have been presented in this section have become progressively more difficult and demanding. Each of the initial exercises focused on a single, isolated aspect of reality, often in a setting or manner designed to minimize distraction. Having familiarized ourselves with each of these aspects in turn, we then began to put them back together into a single piece by viewing them simultaneously. Small children can easily learn to pat their heads or rub their bellies, but find it much more difficult to do both at once; it is the same with us as we attempt to maintain a simultaneous awareness of all six of our sensory fields. Like a juggler who perfects his art until he can juggle six balls at the same time, so too must we patiently practice and perfect our skills.

Attaining a heightened degree of physical and mental coordination, however, is not the end of our difficulty. A reassessment and overhaul of some of our most cherished notions concerning identity and the relationship between the physical body and its environment is also required. In the face of the weight of evidence that has emerged through our inquiry, we begin to see that the notion of "I" is a tenuous one at best and that the division we have created between our physical body and immediate environment is arbitrary and, from the perspective of experience, artificial. It is not that these conventional notions of identity and relationship are necessarily wrong or inapplicable. They are, however, certainly incomplete. They present a single perspective based on the primacy of *conception*. Such an isolated way of looking at things, in spite of its undeniable usefulness, can only serve to further our condition of suffering if not balanced out by a complementary perspective that is grounded in actual *perception*. Such an alternate point of view can guide us back to the experience of union and connectedness (and to the satisfaction which that remembrance generates) that is so lacking in our lives.

In this exercise let us make one last demand, one final observation about the mandala of reality. It is difficult enough to experience the merging and interpenetration of the sensory fields under the best of conditions. Alone in a very remote and beautiful mountain region, for example, we can patiently contemplate a sheer mountain precipice or a towering, ageless tree. The blurring of boundaries and distinctions comes more easily here, and when we return to our homes and families, we do so feeling nourished and enriched. What happens, however, when we come face to face with another person, a fellow human being who we know has every bit as legitimate a claim to the title of "I" as we have ourselves? Such an encounter presents us with an even more arduous test.

What happens when we look directly into another person's eyes and our partner holds and returns our gaze? Initially, there may be a period of discomfort or nervousness, accompanied by a virtually automatic desire to look away. The tactile quadrant of the mandala of reality becomes greatly intensified, and this magnification taxes our ability to accept this field as it is, without reaction. If we are able to get through this initial awkwardness, however, a whole new phase of experience begins to open up. The rigidity and opacity that ordinarily condition the experience of our personal boundaries become significantly softer and more permeable. As our contact with each other continues to deepen, our sense of physical boundary may vanish completely. We will begin to feel drawn into a common vortex of experience, a common ground of being. Just as iron filings are drawn toward a powerful magnetic source, so too do we experience ourselves as being ineluctably drawn closer to a shared awareness of union, relatedness, and the condition of love that naturally accompanies them. In the presence of such a powerful magnetic field, all of the holding and blockage that interfere with our ability to experience this place of deep merging are gradually brought up to the surface of awareness where, if accepted as they are without manipulation, they begin slowly to dissolve.

All that is required of us is that we continue to hold each other's gaze and to surrender to the organic nature of this markedly alchemical process. Each of these places of holding or blockage, when brought to the surface of awareness, can be perceived to be empowered by its own motive force. If we can learn to yield to this force, then the holding and blockage that we experience automatically begin to diminish. If we can allow this force to move us and cause us to respond in whatever manner it sees fit, it eventually dissolves. With each resolution that occurs, we find that we are drawn ever deeper into the shared experience of our common source. It is as though a cloud suddenly lifts, and the brilliance of the sun shows piercingly through.

This common ground that we experience with each other is nothing other than the locus of experience which the last exercise directed us to consider. However, we are now faced with a further revelation, one that makes the image of the mandala of reality truly universal. In the middle of the mandala appears a representation of a human body. Initially it was necessary to identify ourselves with this representation in order to unravel the conventionally tangled web of misperception that obscures the vision to which the mandala alludes. Now we are led to a further understanding that has radical repercussions for our sense of personal identity: the centermost image of the mandala does not refer to a specific human body, but to the whole of humankind. The images that appear in our six sensory fields are different for every person who lives on this planet. The locus of experience, wherein these individual images are integrated, however, is identical. This is not to say that my locus of experience is similar to yours. Rather, it is the same place. At this precise location we gain entrance into the substratum of experience that binds all of humanity together as a single body or organism.

Such a bond cannot be broken, even by denial. While such an understanding runs directly counter to what our common sense would have us believe, it is nonetheless born out by experience.[15] The "facts" are these: When another person and I look into each other's eyes, we are both led to an experience of our centers; as our contact with each other intensifies, we are led to the awareness that our centers are not separate. The ground of individual being, once contacted, is revealed to be "co-terminous" with the ground of universal being.[16] Faced with such evidence, do we acquiesce to the conventions of common sense, or do we forge a new understanding that more accurately reflects the truth of experience? If we look honestly into our own experience, we cannot escape this truth. Neither can we escape the responsibility, or the joy, that accompany its realization.

Holding the gaze of another person can be one of the most potent ways in which this aspect of the mandala of reality can reveal itself. The exercise can be practiced for moments at a time throughout the course of a day, or it can go on uninterrupted for hours or even longer. How far you go with this kind of exploration is mostly a matter of choice. The technique is there and available to all people at all times. You simply have to want to experiment with it and have the good fortune to meet a partner who wants to do the same. In the beginning, it will be helpful to explore this exercise with your partner in a private space. Over time, it may become familiar and comfortable enough to explore in a public setting as well.

While the physical and mental states that you are likely to encounter may appear altered in comparison to your more familiar states of body and mind, the technique contains its own built-in safety mechanisms that insure that it cannot become dangerous; these mechanisms also prevent the possibility of manipulation on the part of one of the participants. If the experience ever becomes too strongly disorienting, either you or your partner will naturally interrupt the contact by averting your gaze, and the intensity will immediately diminish. In the beginning, it may feel highly uncomfortable to practice this exercise. Once you have familiarized yourself with it, however, you may find that this is the only way of relating that feels truly comfortable. Only from this perspective can you come to appreciate the inherent pain that exists in conventional social interaction. From this perspective,

---

15) Common sense is generally a positive trait. Here, however, the word "common" means "ordinary" or "coarse." When our sensory perception is rough and unrefined, we "see" the objects of the world as separate and distinct and forfeit the experience of deep connection and interpenetration that highly refined ("uncommon sense") perception reveals.

16) Frederick Franck, editor, R. H. Blyth, *Zen and Zen Classics* (New York: Random House, 1978), p. 58.

it is your more familiar states of body and mind, prone as they are to nurturing the myths of separation and isolation, that appear truly altered.

While it may appear that we have come far afield from our initial inquiry into the relationship between the physical structure of the body and the gravitational field of the earth, we have actually come full circle. Rightly perceived, the implications of balance spill over into every area of our lives. As we become ever more sensitive to these implications and the experience upon which they are based, we come to realize that the maintenance of balance depends on a complete reexamination of some of our most cherished beliefs and notions about the nature of reality. If these are left unexamined, then our potential for balance becomes limited. If our progression toward a heightened condition of balance is accompanied with an honest examination of these issues, the conclusions that we inevitably reach serve to enhance our ability to remain in balance. Our exploration of balance, through the medium of our bodily experience, has unearthed an alternative way in which to view reality. In its turn, an understanding of this alternative vision provides us with the philosophical reinforcement that we need to maintain that balance.

Starting from purely physical observations, we move rapidly into the arena of metaphysics and then back again. Ida Rolf would often caution us to make sure that we thoroughly understood the physical implications of a problem before we ventured forth into the realm of the metaphysical. Only then could our extended observations have a chance of being accurate reflections of truth. She would also say that what is labeled metaphysics is simply physics yet unproved. Metaphysics becomes physics once its observations are fully understood. That understanding is coming closer. The technology of balance has become highly sophisticated. We have a much clearer understanding of the physical mechanisms that allow for it and the structural principles that underlie it. The proof of its implications is steadily revealing itself through our experience. Building upon just such a stable base, we have no choice but to journey outward.

In Conclusion

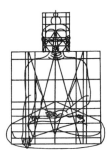

W hile the ideas and exercises that have been presented here can be approached on their own terms without any prior training or exposure to traditional Buddhist or somatic practices, it is highly recommended that any reader who is seriously interested in pursuing these ideas explore these two fields further. Such a foundation will help clarify this material, making it much easier to assimilate the depths of what is being said.

A wide variety of different Buddhist schools from Southeast Asia, Tibet, and Japan all present a slightly different interpretation or version of the original teachings of the Buddha. While the particulars may differ considerably, the essence remains the same throughout. You may wish to experiment with a number of these different approaches until you find the one that best suits your temperament. Ultimately, you may have to tailor even this approach so that it truly fits your needs. Individual approaches and techniques can help lead you to the *dharma*; once you pick up the scent, however, you should follow the trail unfailingly wherever it leads you, even if it means altering the original technique. In general, any exploration of a Buddhist technique will require a sincere commitment in terms of time and energy, but very little, actual monetary expenditure.

One particular technique is worth mentioning here as its approach is so directly compatible with the vision of this book. *Vipassana* meditation in the tradition of U Ba Khin is a Burmese form of Buddhist practice that focuses almost exclusively on the experience of body. To learn this technique you need to attend one of the many ten-day meditation retreats that are held regularly in locations around the world. To receive a schedule of upcoming retreats, contact Vipassana Meditation Center, Dhammadhara, P.O. Box 24, Shelburne Falls, Massachusetts, 01370, U.S.A.

The offerings of somatic therapy are broad and diverse, and new strategies of intervention are appearing constantly. Roughly speaking, there are two main trunks to the somatic tree. The first can be seen as emotional-energetic in origin and stems from the seminal insights of Wilhelm Reich. The goals of the many forms of Reichian and bioenergetic therapy are not incompatible with the goals of Viennese analysis; the difference, and it is a major one, is the focus on the body as the means to freeing the restricted expression of emotion and energetic flow. Reich's original breathing techniques have blossomed in the practices of Rebirthing and, more recently, Holotropic Breathwork, both of which dispense with much of the analytic theory, replacing it instead with a psychological model based on love and acceptance of self.

The other major trunk of the somatic tree is arguably more purist in its somatic orientation. Focusing on the actual physical structure and movement patterns of the body, the work of such figures as Ida Rolf, Matthias Alexander, and Moshe Feldenkrais is far more oriented toward the practical, physical fact of embodiment than it is in the analytic model of the psychotherapeutic establishment. Dance therapy, sensory awareness, the interest in hatha yoga and the martial arts — not only are the approaches to the body virtually limitless, but somatic therapists and teachers are an eclectic breed by nature and often combine many different techniques in their work. While this book has focused primarily on the work of Ida Rolf, nothing that has been said about the body should appear incompatible with any of the other somatic approaches. All of them have their appropriate applications; all of them may be profitably pursued. If you feel drawn to a particular approach, pursue it.

Whenever a new idea becomes popular enough to make a significant impression on the culture in which it has been introduced, it is bound to be distributed, copied, and interpreted. This has been the case in recent years with Ida Rolf's original insights, just as it has happened over centuries to the original teachings of the Buddha. Indeed, the development of modern science and psychology has depended on just such a process of proliferation wherein an original idea, in the form of a seed, gives birth to new ideas or ramifications which, in turn, keep spawning ever new interpretations over time. The two most well-known organizations devoted to Ida Rolf's teachings are the Rolf Institute and the Guild for Structural Integration. To receive a list of Rolfers nearest you, contact the Rolf Institute, P.O. Box 1868, Boulder, Colorado, 80306, U.S.A. To receive a list of Structural Integration practitioners, contact the Guild for Structural Integration, P.O. Box 1559, Boulder, Colorado, 80306, U.S.A. In addition, there have been several individual Rolfers who have established training programs separate from these two main organizations, and it is entirely possible that you will encounter local practitioners whose work derives directly from the teaching of Ida Rolf, but who received their training through one of these individuals rather than through the Institute or the Guild.

How do you go about choosing a practitioner if a choice is possible? In general, it is advisable to meet with the person for an initial interview. This will enable you to get a sense for the person and for his or her particular approach to the work. Some Rolfers, for example, are classical structuralists, focusing solely on body. Others are equally interested in the emotional or energetic issues that keep bodies imbalanced. Depending on your needs, you may find the approach of one or another practitioner more suitable. It is always a good idea to inquire about the training a person has received and how long he or she has been practicing. Entering into a program that can powerfully realign the structure of the body is to embark on a significant chapter in your life. It will be time-consuming, emotionally demanding, and quite often costly. In view of this, it is especially important that the person you decide to work with is someone whose professional understanding you trust and with whom you can establish a comfortable rapport.

Finally, anyone wishing to communicate with the author or to receive information about personal or professional training programs directly related to the vision of this book may do so by contacting The Institute for Embodiment Training, RR 2, Cobble Hill, B.C., V0R 1L0, Canada.